KINGDOMS

— OF —

THE EAST

COLIN WILLOCK

SURVIVAL

ANGLIA
Television Limited

Boxtree

FIRST PUBLISHED 1991 BY BOXTREE LIMITED

© SURVIVAL ANGLIA 1991
TEXT © COLIN WILLOCK 1991
DESIGNED BY KEITH POINTING WITH CELESTE HENNEY
MAPS BY ML DESIGN
COLOUR REPRODUCTION IN HONG KONG BY FOTOGRAPHICS
TYPESET IN BEMBO BY ROWLAND PHOTOTYPESETTING LIMITED, BURY ST EDMUNDS, SUFFOLK
PRINTED AND BOUND IN SPAIN BY CAYFOSA INDUSTRIA GRAFICA, BARCELONA

FOR BOXTREE LIMITED
36 TAVISTOCK STREET
LONDON WC2E 7PB

A CIP CATALOGUE RECORD FOR THIS BOOK
IS AVAILABLE FROM THE BRITISH LIBRARY

ISBN 1-85283-139-1

CONTENTS

INTRODUCTION

'Kingdoms of the East'. The term is, of course, a relative one. It depends where on earth you are standing. It so happened that the early explorers and navigators set out from Europe. East and West in a geographical sense were for ever after viewed from this starting point. Had Australia been the point of departure for Vasco da Gama and Columbus, India and Europe might have been called 'the West' and America 'the East'.

When it comes to the movement and distribution of species, the animal kingdom is not concerned with such niceties. East or West, North or South, it is all the same to the elephant, the orang-

A leopard relaxes up a tree in the heat of the day.

utan or the tiger. All that matters is that, when subjected to pressures beyond its control, a species can move to parts of the globe that are more hospitable and then adapt to the conditions there. If it succeeds, it survives. If it fails, it becomes extinct.

Zoologists recognize that wildlife is not confined by national boundaries or even by continents. So they have overlaid the names geographers have given to countries and continents with six main 'zoogeographical regions'. For example, the Nearctic Region covers North America; the Neotropical Region, Central and South America. In the case of the New World, the zoogeographical regions almost exactly match the continents. Though this cannot always be so neatly arranged, the principle is invariably the same. Broadly speaking, the same species, families and even orders of animals occupy each region.

The Palaearctic covers all of Europe, Russia, the Middle East and Asia Minor. Africa south of the Sahara is called the Ethiopian Region. Lastly, there are the Oriental and Australian Regions. The Oriental Region and the distribution of the animals that live in it are

---

The iridescent blue of a peacock's neck stands out amongst the green 'eyes' of the tail feathers.

the subjects of this book. At this point, it should be said that the distribution of species within zoogeographical regions is not entirely clear-cut. There is, often, some blurring of the picture, an intermingling of the species of one region with those of its neighbour. These areas of wildlife no man's land are known as transitional zones.

Nowhere on earth is this change-over from the wildlife of one zoogeographical region to another more fascinatingly demonstrated than in the East. The true kingdom of the East is, of course, the Oriental Region, which includes the Indian subcontinent, Malaysia, China, Thailand, most of the islands of Indonesia and the Philippines.

However, to tell the amazing story of how the animals of this part of the globe became distributed it is necessary at least to peer over its eastern boundary into the next zoogeographical zone, where the flora and fauna are so totally different they might belong to another world. This last zoogeographical region is the Australian one, which includes New Guinea.

A macaque monkey in its native habitat of Hong Kong.

Between these two wildlife kingdoms is a great divide. It is often called the Wallace Line, after Alfred Wallace, the nineteenth-century naturalist who first described it. The line between the Oriental and Australian animal kingdoms runs down between New Guinea and Borneo and roughly through the Greater Sunda Islands. This is the transitional zone where the wildlife change-over between the two regions takes place. Yet it is not quite as simple as that, for the primates and civets of the Oriental Region mix here with some of the marsupials or pouched animals of Australia.

How have these divisions and intermixing of wildlife species come about? To understand this you have to go back at least 200 million years to when all the land above the surface of the then oceans was massed in one great super-continent that is sometimes called Pangaea, the more southerly part of which is known as Gondwanaland. If they were not actually joined together, then the continents we know today lay in very close proximity. Superficial evidence of this is the jigsaw pattern in which the east coast of South

A pheasant-tailed jacana, wings raised in an aggressive posture.

America fits neatly into the west coast of Africa. It is fairly certain, too, that the present-day southern continents lay closely together: Antarctica against the south-east tip of Africa, the Australian land-mass alongside the southern corner of Antarctica.

There is ample scientific evidence that Gondwanaland took this form. The formation of rocks and the magnetism contained in them show conclusively that the land masses were once joined in this way. There is fossil evidence, also. The dinosaurs once roamed the whole earth. Their fossils are found in every continent, demonstrating that there was once a connection between the land masses. In the last 200 million years the continents have gradually been moving apart. The recent theories of plate tectonics and continental drift explain this. The continents are anchored to plates of basaltic rock that 'float' on the plastic rock of the earth's mantle. The plates move apart, in some places such as along the mid-Atlantic ridge at the rate of as much as an inch a year. This movement gives rise to a number of literally earth-shattering phenomena including volcanic

_Perched on its nest, this spoonbill stands out
sharply against the sunset._

action, earthquakes and the creation of islands and even new seas. The Red Sea, opened up by the gradual shifting of Arabia away from Africa, is a continuing example.

We are concerned in this book with the distribution of animals in the Oriental Region and in the transitional zone between it and its nearest zoogeographical neighbours. Continental drift has played a very large part in that distribution. It has done so by isolating families and even whole orders of animals, such as the marsupials of the Australian Region, in a continent that has been cast adrift like a giant lifeboat for 130 million years.

Continental drift has also pushed up great mountain ranges as the result of one land mass colliding with another. The Himalayas arose in this way and have proved an insuperable barrier to animal movement ever since. Continental movements also opened up the Indian Ocean and thus cut off all animal communication with the south.

A large cross-tusker elephant in Sri Lanka, displaying the versatility of its trunk.

The process of continental drift is never-ending. There is plain evidence at this moment that the Kingdoms of the East are once again coming closer together on the earth's moving plates. The Australian plate is steadily moving north-east. What the effect will be on their inhabitants, wildlife or human, if indeed any of either remain, we will have to wait perhaps 100 million years to find out.

Almost two hundred years ago, there was one great super-continent known as Pangaea (top map). Today we know that the landmasses sit on moving plates that 'float' on the rock of the earth's mantle. This map shows how the continents came to be where they are today and where they will rest in the future (lower map).

(Overleaf) – Gol-Oya National Park, Sri Lanka, where the Gol-Oya River was dammed to create a great lake.

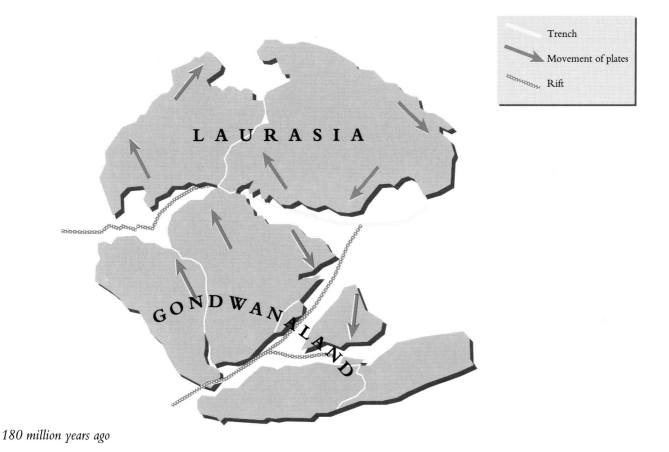

LAURASIA

GONDWANALAND

180 million years ago

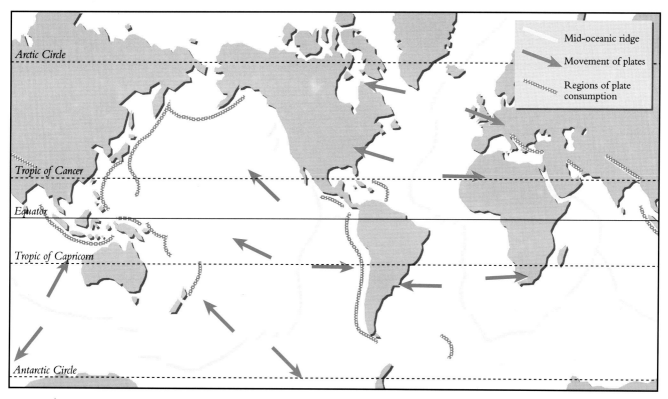

Arctic Circle

Tropic of Cancer

Equator

Tropic of Capricorn

Antarctic Circle

Present day

1

'TYGER, TYGER . . .'

IF an election could be held to decide which animal was to reign over of the Kingdoms of the East there would be three leading candidates. The lion still lives in India in small numbers. The elephant is widely distributed over much of Asia though the population is dwindling. But lions and elephants exist in other zoogeographical regions, too. The tiger, however, roams only the jungles of the East. The tiger has a mystique, majesty and power that man has always respected, revered and feared, immortalized by William Blake when he wrote:

> Tyger, tyger burning bright
> In the forests of the night.
> What immortal hand or eye
> Could frame thy fearful symmetry?

How did this greatest and most awe-inspiring of the great cats come to make the East its special domain?

The generally accepted theory is that the ancestors of the tiger originated in the cold and barren lands of Siberia and northern Asia. The southward march of the ice in the Pleistocene, which is to say during the last two or three million years, forced the animal southward in search of prey. This migration outflanked the Himalayan barrier by moving down through Manchuria and China. When they reached South-East Asia, some of these ancestral animals continued on southward into what is now Malaysia, Burma and Indonesia. Some crossed the island chain through Sumatra, Java and as far east as Bali.

Westward, the other branch of this great movement occupied India. Outflanking the Himalayas, this time on the western side, some ancestral tigers carried on north towards the shores of the Caspian Sea. There are, however, no tigers in Sri Lanka, so they must have reached the southern tip of India when the land bridge to that island had disappeared and the sea gap become too wide for even a tiger to swim across. Supporters of this generally held theory point to the tiger's thick fur and heavy layer of fat; also to its need to keep cool in the hot climates in which it now lives by immersing itself in water whenever it can during the heat of the day.

Opponents point out that it is highly unlikely that the prototype tiger would have needed to develop stripes if it had originated in the open spaces of the barren and chilly north. An interesting counter-theory is put forward by Nicholas Courtney in his book *The Tiger, Symbol of Freedom*. He argues that the tiger, the lion and the leopard, all of the same genus, *Panthera*, had a common ancestor, the prehistoric cave lion, also of that genus. It was this animal that was forced south by

the ice. Its descendants evolved in quite different ways. The lion adapted itself to dry, open grassland where a yellow coat was most effective. The leopard's spots provided excellent camouflage in the wide range of habitats in which it successfully lived.

The tiger gained its stripes by evolving in dense jungle and wet, reedy areas. There is certainly a marked similarity between the fossilized skulls of early lions, leopards and the cave lions, though the tiger's is rather more dome-shaped than the rest. If this theory is right, then the presence of tigers in Siberia today is accounted for by the fact that when the ice relented and moved northward again, the tiger, complete with its new stripes, followed in search of fresh fields and new sources of prey. This still does not account satisfactorily for the tiger's thick fur and the need to keep itself cool in its oriental habitat. Surely it does not need this insulation even during the chilliest nights in the jungle?

On the other hand, if the tiger did originate in the frozen north, why have today's Siberian tigers such a rufous striped coat? If they evolved among the snows, surely those that still live there would have learned to acquire a white covering, at least in winter, like the Arctic fox, the ptarmigan and

(Previous page) In the jungles of southern Asia the tiger has evolved a perfect camouflage.

Tigers are solitary animals. The only stable group is formed by a tigress and her cubs (right).

the snowshoe hare. It is a fascinating source of speculation.

Whichever theory is correct, we can only be sure of the distribution of the tiger today, or rather the day before yesterday. The tiger is disappearing throughout much of its range and in some areas has already disappeared. At the beginning of this century it is likely that there were 40,000 tigers in India and probably 100,000 throughout the rest of Asia. No one can be quite sure of the actual numbers, though it was certainly not less than this estimate. Today there may be only 5,000 left, and the total is shrinking all the time.

There are, or rather were, eight races of tiger, all slightly different in size or density and coloration of the striped coat. Tigers still exist in China (very limited numbers in Fukien and Shensi Pro-

vinces); Siberia, where they are well protected; Indo-China, with possibly as many as 2,000; India and Nepal, 2,000; Sumatra, up to 800; Java, only a handful, if any, left. There are occasional rumours of tigers in the region of the Caspian Sea but no confirmed sightings. Like the Balinese tiger, the smallest of the eight races, the Caspian tiger is probably no more.

The tiger is without doubt the most awesome and magnificent of the big cats. Throughout the Far East, the tiger has always been regarded as an animal of magical properties. In Malaysia, a single tiger whisker ground up in the animal's flesh or bone is thought to be powerful enough to kill an enemy. In Taiwan they drink wine made from tiger bone. The wine is said to give the drinker special strength. The Chinese believe that the clavicle, a small bone embedded in the shoulder muscle, is a protection against evil. When the British came to India they, too, fell under the spell of the mystical tiger, believing it to be an inveterate man-hunter. It was said that the main fear of many army officers who were posted to India was that they would be eaten by a tiger. All this is superstition. The facts of the tiger's existence are impressive enough without adding legend to them.

In the tiger, evolution has produced a perfect hunting machine. The striped markings enable the beast to become invisible against a wide range of backgrounds by day or night. The patterning of stripes varies from animal to animal. Generally, the tigers of the south are smaller and darker than those further north. The distinctive and beautiful face with white patches below the ears provides as

One theory says that tigers evolved in the far north. If so, why the stripes? The white coat of the Arctic fox (left) would have been more suitable. The Siberian tiger, largest of its kind (right). Did it arrive complete with stripes when its ancestors moved north? (right). Tigers are the most aquatic of the big cats. They spend much of their time in water keeping cool (overleaf).

good camouflage as the rest of the body. Viewed head-on from short range the animal is exceedingly hard to spot, provided it stands still. The only other white markings on the upper body are two spots on the back of the ears. It has been suggested that these are used in aggressive display. However, an angry or attacking tiger lays its ears back and surely a mere flashing of the ears cannot add much to the general appearance of anger and aggression mirrored in the whole body of the beast. It is more likely that the white ear spots are there as a signal to cubs following their dam in thick jungle. But then why should a male have spots? Male tigers play very little part in bringing up their young.

The weight of the biggest tiger shot by the Maharaja of Nepal was 705 lb (320 kg). However, the average male tiger weighs 400–500 lb (180–225 kg) and the female up to 100 lb (45 kg) less. An adult tiger stands at least 3 ft (90 cm) high at the shoulder. As to length, there are two traditional ways of measuring and both owe their origins to tiger shooting. The first was called 'over curves'. In this method a tape measure was run from tip of tail to nose following the lines of the beast's back. There were obvious ways in which the measurement could be stretched to the advantage of the shooter. The more reliable method was 'between pegs'. The dead tiger was laid on its back and pegs driven into the ground at nose and tip of outstretched tail. The body was then moved and the distance between pegs measured. Maharajas' game-books record tigers of 10 ft 9 in (3.3 m) between pegs. A lot plainly depended on the length of the animal's tail, which can vary by as much as 15 in (40 cm). Nowadays when tigers are 'shot' and measured it is almost always by research scientists. The worst that the animal suffers is the after-effects of the anaesthetic from a dart gun.

Tigers contact each other by roaring, a vocalisation shared with lions and, to a lesser extent, with leopards. This tiger is merely yawning.

So long as a tiger stands still or moves slowly, its stripes make it practically invisible in the jungle or among reeds.

Though the tiger at speed possesses the most fluid movement of all the big predators, when it ambles along it is almost ungainly. The reason is that at slow speeds it moves both legs on the same side of the body forward at the same time, first one side and then the other. This gives it a peculiar rolling gait. But once it accelerates it adopts the normal movement of any quadruped. When running flat-out, only one foot touches the ground at any one moment.

The power for the spring comes from the back legs and feet. An attacking leap can carry the animal 10 yards (9 m) until its front feet strike ground or prey. The energy generated by such an attack is sufficient to knock over a domestic or wild buffalo weighing a ton (1 tonne). Victims first know that they are marked down as the tiger's next meal when those enormously powerful front feet hit them. The legs that deliver that blow are in proportion to the rest of the tiger's body, the circumference of the upper joint often being as much as 21 in (54 cm). Once the attack has been made, the tiger's secondary armament comes into play, if we can describe as secondary anything as formidable as the animal's four canine teeth. The two in the upper jaw are up to 5 in (13 cm) long. Those in the lower are smaller since two-thirds of these canines are enclosed in the gum. If the prey is not already dead, the canines finish the job. Larger animals are usually suffocated by biting the throat. Smaller animals are killed by biting the back of the neck.

Silence is one of the hunting tiger's greatest attributes. It is extraordinary that such a large animal can move through close cover without revealing itself to its prey. It is well equipped with its own sharp protective senses, especially hearing.

If the prey is running or struggling, the claws come into play. The tiger has five in each of its front feet and four in its rear feet. All are retractile. They are normally sheathed but when hunting they can be extended to a length of 2½ in (6 cm). The final weapon is the tongue, which is as rough as a rasp and is used for stripping hair and skin from the flesh, though the tiger eats plenty of both, probably as roughage. Hearing plays a vital part in the tiger's hunting equipment. In some parts of the East, trackers used to cut the hairs in their nostrils lest the noise of air passing through these as they breathed should alert the tiger to their presence.

Much has been made of the tiger's appetite for human flesh. The truth is that real man-eaters, those tigers that deliberately and consistently hunt human prey, are extremely rare. Tigers do kill and eat people, but there is almost always a reason. The animal may have been wounded or simply have deteriorated so much that it is no longer able to catch deer and other prey. Lost and broken canines and worn-out claws can contribute to this situation. Most man-eaters turn out to be tigresses. One reason for this is that, unlike lions, which hunt as a pride and can therefore support each other, all tigers are loners. A tigress

A tranquillized tiger is fitted with a radio collar so that its movements in Chitawan National Park can be studied.

with cubs is on her own. If food is short and she is desperate to feed her family she has an obvious motive for taking available and easy prey. There is some evidence that a tigress who has killed humans abandons the habit once her family is self-supporting.

Jim Corbett, the hunter-conservationist, after whom one of India's National Parks is named, maintained that man-eaters are made and not born. No one hunted man-eating tigers more assiduously and successfully or knew more about them than Corbett. Man-eating, he claimed, was not hereditary. Even if cubs had been reared on

Young tigers are dependent on their mothers for at least 18 months, after which the family (left) breaks up. The tiger's prey – a herd of swamp deer in Dudwa National Park, India.

human flesh, they did not persist in man-eating once they had grown up. His books such as *The Man-eaters of Rudraprayag* have become minor classics. Corbett was not only a great hunter and practical naturalist, he was also that rare thing, a natural writer.

That tigers have a sense of smell is demonstrated by their ability to detect the scent-mark of other tigers and particularly of females in season. However, scent does not seem to play a large part in hunting. The two senses of taste and smell, which are closely allied, are secondary to hearing and eyesight. The tiger has in-depth vision that is particularly tuned to detecting movement. Like most nocturnal hunters, it possesses a highly developed optical system that can reflect the dullest ray of light through the pupils. This reflection lights up the eyes in the rays of the moon or a lamp to such an extent that some native peoples believe that the tiger's eyes actually generate their own light at night.

The tiger's front paws are its main hunting weapon. This tiger (above) licks its paw with its large, rasping tongue. The purpose of the white ear spots is uncertain but they can be seen very clearly here (right).

When it comes to choice of prey the tiger, like many predators, is an opportunist. Zoo tigers will pick out offal in preference to other flesh. In the wild, tigers appear to consider everything simply as meat. On a kill they show no special relish for liver, heart or kidneys by singling them out to eat first as delicacies. When other meat is scarce they are not above eating carrion in an advanced state of decomposition, which suggests that their olfactory system is not particularly sensitive.

Deer provide the tiger with most of its prey. It takes very little more energy to kill, say, a sambar, the largest of the Asian deer species—a sambar stag can weigh up to 700 lb (320 kg)—than a tiny muntjac or hog deer. Killing a sambar can mean that the tiger does not have to hunt again for up to a week. A chital hind may last only a day but a chital stag weighing up to 200 lb (90 kg) will feed a tiger for two or three days. On rare occasions an experienced tiger will kill a wild buffalo or gaur, the Asian wild ox, weighing up to a ton (1 tonne), but it is far more likely to tackle the young of the larger and powerful species, including elephants and rhinos.

Even a predator as powerful as a tiger wants to avoid risk of damage to itself. When injured it becomes a less efficient hunting machine and puts itself in considerable danger. Tigers are catholic in their taste; they have been known to eat frogs and will sometimes catch fish.

In captivity tigers are prolific breeders. Sadly, the same is not true in the wild. As the result of recent research, mainly in India and Nepal, more and more is being learned about the animal's needs and habits. Alas, this knowledge comes at a

time when it is virtually the eleventh hour for the tiger. Except at mating time, tigers are solitary animals. A dominant male controls a territory of anything from 25 to 250 square miles (65–650 sq km). Inside this are the home ranges of several females. There may also be some junior males trying to muscle in on the dominant male's kingdom. The females do not defend their home ranges but both they and the males regularly scent-mark the boundaries of their areas by spraying bushes with a powerful mixture of urine and scent. This system of communication works very well, especially when a female is in season.

Tigers also contact each other by means of roaring, a form of vocalization that they share with other members of the genus *Panthera*, namely lions and to a lesser extent leopards. The true cats of the genus *Felis* have a different attachment of the larynx that robs them of this ability. In tigers, leopards and lions, the hyoid bone of the larynx is joined to the base of the skull by an elastic ligament. True cats have instead a series of

short bones, placed end to end. The elastic ligament allows a far greater range of vocalization, including roaring and coughing.

Some naturalists believe that tigers will mate at any time of year. In northern India, at least, most pairings occur between November and December or May and June. Courtship and mating in the wild have rarely been seen. Observation of zoo animals and the few accounts from naturalists in the field suggest they are a fairly stormy procedure, consisting of mock chases, vicious swipes of the female's paw as well as obvious kisses and caresses. What is certain is that actual copulation only takes a matter of ten or fifteen seconds, though it may be repeated twenty or more times within twenty-four hours and one hundred times within three or four days. After mating, the male takes no further interest in his mate or her cubs.

(Above) A so-called 'white' tiger; there is only one record of a truly albino tiger. Tiger country in Dudwa National Park (right).

40

As in lions, there is a short gestation lasting from fourteen to sixteen weeks. The cubs weigh 2–3 lb (1–1.5 kg) at birth and are blind. There are usually two or three in a litter. The tigress suckles them for the first six months, by which time they will weigh 100 lb (45 kg). When she weans them on to meat she usually feeds them from the kill before she herself eats. The young tigers are dependent on their mother for at least eighteen months, until the family starts to break up. On the whole, tigresses are unsuccessful mothers. Lions rear as many as half the cubs born to them, largely due to the support that the rest of the pride gives. Tiger mothers are on their own and are nothing like so well protected. They raise fewer than half the cubs born to them. Billy Arjan Singh (see page 47), one of India's leading conservationists and tiger authorities, estimates that, allowing for a breeding life of fifteen years, a wild tigress only rears from five to seven and a half cubs. This is not a high rate of regeneration when all the present-day threats to the tiger are taken into account.

Though several tigers are sometimes found together because, perhaps, prey is particularly abundant in that area, tigers are essentially solitary. The only stable group is that of a tigress and her cubs.

Where the ranges of the tiger and the Asian lion overlap, it has been known for the two to interbreed. This is possible because *Panthera leo persica*, the lion of India, is of the same genus as *Panthera tigris tigris*. When a tigress mates with a lion the result is known as a 'liger'. Reverse the species and you have a 'tigron'. Unfortunately, like all hybrids, these exceptional rarities are infertile. There is only one record of a true albino tiger, though there have been many cream-coloured animals. The most famous of these are the so-called white tigers of Rewa. A nearly white male was captured in the forests of the Maharaja of Rewa in 1951 and mated with a normally coloured tigress. Many of their descendants have since been presented to zoos around the world.

A big male tiger relaxes in a river.

OPERATION TIGER

It is tempting to think of hunting as the main reason for the tiger's decline. Hunting began with the Mogul emperors, who pursued the tiger from elephant and horseback and killed it with spears and bows and arrows. The Moguls can have made very little impression on the total population however. Serious hunting began in the early nineteenth century, when tiger shooting became an obsession with the maharajas and nabobs who quickly passed the mania on to the British officials and army officers. One of the most successful British hunters of the Victorian era was George Yule of the Bengal Civil Service. In twenty-five years his tally reached 400. After that he no longer bothered to keep count. There were, it is true, plenty of tigers to hunt, but the numbers killed are almost un-believable. Among the maharajas tiger shooting became highly competitive. For visiting dignitaries it was practically obligatory to shoot a tiger. Subalterns posted to the Indian Army were expected to kill a tiger in order to prove that they were made of the right stuff.

The mania persisted into the present century. Individual scores became a status symbol. Cubs and even foetuses cut from the bodies of pregnant females were added to individual hunters' totals. One of the top scorers, the Maharaja of Sarguja claimed 1,150 tigers. His close rival, the Maharaja of Rewa, reached a total of 500 and then withdrew from the contest. Many others reached the 500 mark. The Maharaja Joodha Shamser Jung accounted for 433 tigers in just four seasons. As late as the 1930s, the Prime Minister of Nepal killed 295 tigers in seven seasons.

During the heyday of the British Raj, the slaughter was to some extent controlled. The *shikar*, or hunt, was bound by strict rules. Licences for fire-arms were issued under careful control and the hunting confined to a privileged few. The method of hunting varied according to the nature of the country. In dense jungle or tall grass the shooting was usually done from elephant back, a comparatively safe exercise except when a cornered tiger sprang at the *howdah* in which the *shikari* and his gun-bearer were poised on the elephant. More hazardous was the method used in the open country of central India, in which a line of beaters drove the tiger, or often tigers, past concealed hunters. Sometimes a large semi-circle of white sheets was constructed at the end of the drive to stop the tiger escaping past the guns. The cheapest and most practical method was for the *shikari* to sit out over a tethered bait in a tree hide or *machan* waiting for the tiger to appear.

After The Second World War the situation changed sharply for the worse. Independence led to the abolition of feudal privileges. Now,

Honoured guests were expected to shoot tigers. This hunt was held in honour of King George V (third from the right, front row) during his Durbar Tour in 1911.

anyone could shoot a tiger. The rules that the British and the maharajas had created to protect their sport were seen as an evil of colonialism. Cultivation spread to the edge of forests that had previously been the tiger's domain, and the forests themselves were clear-felled. Deprived of prey, the tiger naturally encroached on farm land to feed on the deer attracted by the crops as well as to kill domestic stock. Crop-protection licences were issued wholesale, with disastrous results for the tiger. Many were poisoned or trapped as crop raiders, and if anyone needed an incentive, high prices were paid for skins. It looked as though the end of the trail had come for the tiger.

The World Wildlife Fund, in 1988 renamed the Worldwide Fund for Nature, has been criticized, largely unjustly in my view, for not saving endangered species such as the African elephant, the panda and the black rhino. In the case of the elephant and rhino it is difficult to see what the Fund could have done, other than supply anti-poaching equipment and finance for wardens. The survival or otherwise of a threatened species depends in the end on the will and determination of the country concerned. In the campaign to save the tiger, the Fund certainly played its part, greatly helped by the fact that it enjoyed the wholehearted support of the leader of the country most involved.

In 1969 the plight of the tiger was at last officially recognized. The total number in India was thought to have fallen to 2,500, with perhaps another thousand elsewhere. At a meeting of

Billy Arjan Singh (left) takes a walk in the jungle with Tara, the tigress whom he returned to the wild.

the International Union for the Conservation of Nature (IUCN) in Delhi the Indian tiger was added to the list of endangered species in the famous, or perhaps infamous, IUCN Red Data Book.

A ban on hunting was imposed by all the governments of countries and states in which the Indian tiger occurred. The export of skins was prohibited. If the fight to get these bans imposed was a hard one, the enforcement of the ban was even harder. Penalties were small compared with the price paid for tiger skins. The *shikar* lobby was strong and well organized and naturally argued that the tiger population was holding its own.

It became essential to obtain an accurate estimate of just how many tigers were left. In 1972 5,000 researchers in two huge operations took a census and came up with the figure of 1,872 tigers for the whole of India.

At this point, Guy Mountfort, a founder member of the World Wildlife Fund, prepared a scheme for saving the tiger called 'Operation Tiger'. The obstacles to this were largely financial: it was said to be beyond the means of the WWF, let alone the Government of India. A world appeal for one million dollars was launched. It produced 1.7 million!

What sceptics said would be the hardest part of the enterprise still lay ahead—persuading the Indian Government to back the scheme. In the event, this was practically a walkover. Mountfort had carefully paved the way in meetings with the Prime Minister, Mrs Indira Gandhi, who not only gave her complete support but appointed a cabinet minister as well as the director of Delhi Zoo to supervise a six-year conservation plan. Two million pounds was voted for 'Project Tiger', as the Indian version of the WWF operation was called, an incredible sum in view of India's other economic problems at the time.

'Project Tiger', launched on 1 April 1973, initially established eleven reserves, each in a different state with a different kind of tiger habitat. There were also 125 smaller reserves, including Billy Arjan Singh's Tiger Haven at Dudwa near the India–Nepal border (see page 64).

Guy Mountfort next persuaded Bangladesh, despite the fact that the country was at a low ebb due to the recent war, to allocate part of the Sunderbans, the marshes of the Ganges Delta, as a tiger reserve. Together with the reserve in the Indian part of the Sunderbans, this formed one of the largest wildlife reserves in the entire orient.

The Nepalese government quickly fell in with the World Wildlife Fund's proposals for 'Operation Tiger' and designated 210 square miles (545 sq km) of the Royal Chitawan National Park as a sanctuary for tigers, later enlarged to 360 square miles (930 sq km) with the aid of the Frankfurt

Tiger tracks. Each footprint is nearly six inches (15 cm) wide.

Tara, three quarters grown, crosses the river with Babulal, one of Billy Arjan Singh's helpers.

Zoological Society. It is at Chitawan that much of the recent research work into the habits of the tiger has been carried out both by Dr Chuck McDougal, director of wildlife activities at the famous Tiger Tops Lodge, and by Nepali and American scientists funded by the Smithsonian Institute in Washington.

About thirty sub-adult tigers there were darted and fitted with radio collars so that their movements could be monitored, sometimes from a light aircraft but often from elephant back! Accurate pictures could now be built up for the first time as to how tigers spent their day, how often they killed, their associations with other tigers and how the young animals found and established their own home ranges. This last piece of information was particularly important for establishing how much territory an increasing tiger population in any area would need.

There is an interesting link between the setting up of reserves such as Chitawan and what some may see as the bad old days of tiger hunting. In almost every case, and in India and Nepal certainly, the only areas in which tigers continued to exist in any quantities were former hunting reserves. True, tigers have been protected there in the past for the purpose of sport. Even more important was that the jungle habitat had been protected for the same reason. Without protection of its habitat, no animal can survive and in no case is this more true than that of a large predator like the tiger.

Other countries have followed India and Nepal's lead, but in some cases it is already too late. Scientists estimate that a gene pool of at least 300 animals is necessary to maintain a healthy tiger population. Obviously, these tigers have to be able to make regular contact with each other, yet there are very few reserves that satisfy this requirement.

There have been, it must be admitted, one or two unfortunate side-effects of 'Operation Tiger' as a result of its success. Where tiger numbers have increased and the size of the reserve has stayed the same, there has been an overspill of tigers into areas of human occupation. A fully adult male needs a large home range and young males often establish their own on the fringe of the reserve. The result is inevitably a clash, sometimes fatal, with livestock and even humans.

The most dramatic examples of this have occurred in the Sunderbans. The delta is frequented by fishermen and woodcutters as well as by a healthy population of tigers. Some of these have developed a taste for human flesh, perhaps as a result of feeding on bodies washed down by the Ganges during the ever more frequent floods. (The floods, incidentally, are increasingly catastrophic because of the poor or non-existent conservation policy in the catchment areas where the forests have been recklessly and wantonly felled. Without forests and ground cover, the rain simply runs off into the rivers. Thus the lack of forestry conservation that ultimately drowns humans is precisely the same as that which robs tigers of their homes over much of the East.)

To return to the problems of the Sunderbans, the 500 tigers who live there are, owing to the flooded nature of the delta, more than usually aquatic. They also appear to be more than usually keen on human prey. Fishermen sleeping in their boats anchored several hundred yards offshore have been taken by swimming tigers. A number of woodcutters and honey-hunters have fallen victim to Sunderbans tigers. More than thirty people a year are killed there. Apart from the human loss of life this is obviously bad publicity for the tiger, who is being protected by the goodwill of the Bangladesh and Indian governments.

In an effort to curb the man-eaters some very strange ruses have recently been attempted, including putting out dummy woodcutters wired up to give an electric shock. Tigers have attacked the dummies and torn them apart without any sign of being discouraged by the sharp jolt they have received.

Since tigers are said usually to attack humans from the rear, Sunderbans workers have been issued with plastic face masks to be worn on the back of the head. This device seems to have worked. The year after these were introduced, no one wearing a back-to-front mask was killed but thirty people who were not protected in this way fell victim to tigers.

Back in the 1950s Jim Corbett gave the tiger ten years before it became extinct. Mercifully, he was wrong, but despite everything that is being done to protect this greatest of predators, it is very doubtful if its lease of life in the wild can be extended very much longer.

2

THE CAT THAT

WALKS ALONE

IF the explanation of the evolution and distribution of the lion, tiger and leopard is correct, then the leopard spread out further and more successfully than the other two members of its genus.

Today, leopards range widely from West Africa to Sumatra. They were once fairly abundant in the mountainous regions of North Africa, too. Their smaller size—an adult male weighs around 150 lb (70 kg) and a female perhaps 30 lb (14 kg) less—makes them more adaptable than either the lion or the tiger, as does their athleticism. Leopards can run, jump, climb trees and swim with equal ease. They have few demands beyond a supply of food and water. They do not need to kill large animals in order to live. They are equally at home in dense forest, sparse woodland, savanna, or even on rocky hillsides. Their spotted camouflage is effective in any of these settings. It is no coincidence that combat soldiers, particularly paratroops, wear camouflage uniforms that somewhat resemble a leopard's spotted coat.

That the leopard still survives across such a wide range is due not only to its remarkable gifts of concealment but also to its secretive lifestyle.

With very few exceptions—and we shall come to one of the most remarkable of these in this chapter—it is a nocturnal hunter. The day is spent in a tree or in a den, perhaps on a rocky hillside.

The leopard, like the other great spotted cat of the East, the tiger, is on the decline. The reasons in each case are the same: the sheer weight of human expansion and overpopulation. The same spotted coat that conceals the leopard so successfully has also been its undoing. Until recent years, leopard skins fetched high prices in the fur trade. Now the 106 member states belonging to CITES (the Convention on International Trade in Endangered Species) have imposed a ban on the import and export of the skins of spotted cats. Conservation propaganda has made fashionable women genuinely ashamed to be seen wearing a

The 'rosette' markings of a leopard's coat vary in size across the head and body.

Leopards are great tree climbers, often carrying prey as heavy as themselves into the branches (above).

A leopard and her cub. Leopard cubs are weaned at three months and then share their mother's kills.

(Overleaf) This young leopard has already mastered the art of finding a tree perch which provides a sheltered and comfortable position for surveillance of the land.

(Above) Trade in the skins of spotted cats is banned internationally. It takes up to seven skins to make one coat. (Left) Although usually called a panther, this large cat is really a leopard in black or 'melanistic' phase.

leopard-skin coat. However, Conventions, even ones backed by most of the nations of the world, have never totally succeeded in stamping out illegal trading in lucrative contraband. Leopards still die for their skins and it takes five to seven leopards to provide the material for one fur coat!

How successfully the leopard has adapted to a wide range of habitat may be judged from the fact that there are twenty-four different subspecies all of which differ only slightly in colouring or body size and shape. There is, however, only one basic leopard, *Panthera pardus*. Even the panther is really a leopard, albeit a black one. It is confined to the forests of South-East Asia. Though the panther's coat looks totally black, in certain lights it can be seen to be patterned with even darker spots. The name 'panther' comes from its genetic classification. The more general term 'leopard' is far less scientifically based, being a contraction of *leo* and *pardus*, 'lion' and 'panther'.

The basic leopard is spotted almost from nose to tail. On the greater part of the body the spots are grouped in rosettes. The Old Testament prophet Jeremiah was right when he said of an unlikely event that you might as well expect a leopard to change its spots. A leopard's spots remain unchanged during its lifetime. Moreover the pattern is as individual to each animal as fingerprints are to a person.

The camouflage not only works well among trees, scrub or rocks, but also hides its wearer as efficiently by night as it does by day. The golden, spotted coat mirrors the dappled sunlight of the forest. In moonlight the white belly fur breaks up the outline of the hunter to perfection. Only two areas completely lack the spotted pattern, the underside of the 3-ft (90 cm) tail and the backs of the ears. It shares ear markings with the tiger, very probably for the same reason, to provide a signal for the cubs to follow, especially at night, when their mother leads them through dense jungle. However, as with the tiger, there seems no easy explanation for their purpose.

Like the tiger, the leopard relies on stealth when hunting. An Indian poet once wrote that the tiger stalks the jungle like the lowering clouds of an approaching storm but the leopard moves as silently as mist drifting on a dawn wind.

Leopards have two basic methods of attack. Usually they stalk and spring like the tiger but they are such skilful climbers that a branch overhanging a game trail provides the perfect place of ambush from which to leap onto the prey below. Once a leopard has killed, its instinct is to make its meal secure from rivals and scavengers. Leopards have been known to carry a kill half as heavy again as themselves high into the branches of a tree.

Like any other predator, leopards when hunting seek to get the maximum return for the minimum expenditure of energy. Burn up too many calories catching your food and you simply need more food to replace them. So, the bigger the kill the better.

A leopard will on occasion tackle a sambar, the largest of the Asian deer. The beautifully spotted chital, or axis deer, at around 200 lb (90 kg) is ideal leopard prey. Chital are extremely wary animals that alert each other to danger with a whistling call. When it comes to sounding the alarm, they have an ally in the forest clearings. Monkeys dislike the presence of leopards intensely. Leopards are after all quite as at home in the treetops as they are and on occasion are partial to monkey. Grey langurs seem to have a particular aversion to leopards and call loudly to warn all the other inhabitants of the jungle, including the deer, that a leopard is on the prowl.

Wild piglets are a favourite leopard snack. There are, however, considerable risks involved. The parent pigs guard their families closely. A boar weighing up to 500 lb (225 kg) and armed with sharp, slashing tusks is a highly dangerous adversary.

While filming for the 'Survival' series of television documentaries on wildlife, cameraman Dieter Plage captured on film a unique sequence showing one such encounter. Sri Lanka is the best place in the East to film hunting leopards because, quite exceptionally, the leopards of the island hunt in daylight. The reason that they are diurnal, rather than nocturnal, hunters, is that they are the main predator. Since there are no tigers in Sri Lanka the leopards have nothing to fear from more powerful predators, either in terms of danger to themselves or having their prey stolen.

On this occasion, Plage was set up over a water-hole in a clearing in the jungle, hoping that a leopard would show up to hunt or drink. After a wait of an hour or two he saw a big male stalking on the forest edge. It was plainly a hungry leopard, for it was creeping up on an unsuspecting black-naped hare, an animal that would hardly have provided more than a couple of mouthfuls. At the last moment the hare sensed the danger and bounded off into the undergrowth.

The leopard now switched his attention to the open, sandy space leading to the water. A good 100 yards (90 m) away from him, at the water's edge, was a family of wild pigs, a boar and sow with six or seven piglets. It seemed impossible that the leopard could cross that open space, on which grew only a few clumps of coarse grass, without being seen.

The leopard flattened his belly to the ground and began to creep forward. Amazingly, the pigs did not spot him. At about 30 yards' (27 m) range, he began his charge, relying on speed to get him to the target before the pigs knew what was about to hit them. He nearly made it, but at the last moment the big boar looked up and put in his own charge. The impact of the boar's body rolled that leopard over and over all the way back to the forest edge and finally threw him up into the air in a somersault.

The hunter was very lucky to get away with his life. The author met the leopard a couple of days later on a forest track looking very sorry for himself and with a broken tail!

Leopards are by no means always so ambitious in choosing their victims. Some leopards specialize in catching birds. When all else fails they will eat reptiles, including monitor lizards and sometimes even fish. The normal method of killing is to grip the prey by the throat. Larger animals with the speed and power to escape are grappled by the hindquarters until the leopard can seize the throat.

The spotted axis, or chital, deer is the ideal prey for a leopard.

The pattern of spots is as individual as a person's finger prints. The main body spots are grouped in rosettes.

Except when wounded or cornered, leopards will not often attack a human. In cornered situations they are, however, lethal animals. Their speed and agility make them extremely hard to kill. At close quarters a rifle is almost useless. A shotgun loaded with buckshot is the best weapon for anyone who has the unfortunate task of dispatching a wounded leopard in a confined space or thick cover. Wounds inflicted by a leopard's normally retractile claws require instant treatment. Fragments of rotting flesh lodged under the claws pose a high risk of septicaemia.

You might expect leopards to keep away from forest tracks frequented by humans but they often use them for preference. Tracks make for much easier travelling in thick jungle, and the soft soil greatly aids silent movement. In thick undergrowth, not even a leopard can avoid making some noise.

If you could follow a leopard as it makes its way along such a track or even through the jungle itself, you would see that the animal blazes its own trail every 20 yards (18 m) or so by spraying trees and bushes with its scent mark. As with the tiger it is the male's warning to rivals to stay off its home range. Females declare their presence or availability when in season in exactly the same way.

A leopardess heavy with young is at an obvious disadvantage when it comes to hunting, so nature compensates for this by making her pregnancy a short one of 90-105 days. This short gestation means that, like the kittens of a domestic cat, the cubs are born blind and helpless. This has its advantages for the mother. In the first week after the birth, she can safely leave her litter of up to six cubs, though more usually three, hidden in the den and helpless to move around on their

Swamp deer and grey langurs at a waterhole, a perfect site for a leopard ambush. Adult wild pigs (bottom) can defend themselves but their piglets are a favourite leopard snack.

own, while she hunts. Their eyes open around the ninth day. On their mother's milk, the cubs double their birth weight in four weeks and treble it in six. They are weaned in three months and then share their mother's kills.

At four months they are encouraged to follow their mother on her nightly hunt, though she makes them stay still and hidden during the final stalk to avoid spooking the prey. By the time they are two years old they are sufficiently jungle-wise to live a completely independent life and find home ranges for themselves. By this stage they will be self-supportive competent and efficient hunters.

The leopard has one other smaller relative in the Far East. It lives in Borneo, Sumatra and Java. The clouded leopard measures 3 ft (1 m) from head to rump, about the length of the larger leopard's tail. Its own tail is nearly as long as its body. Like the leopard it uses this as an aid to balance when climbing and leaping. The coat is a yellowish grey with large, handsome grey blotches, the 'clouds' that give it its name. It is a nocturnal hunter preying mainly on birds and small mammals. Zoologists have found the animal difficult to classify in either the genus *Felis* or *Panthera* and have given it a new genus, hence *Neofelis nebula*.

In size the clouded leopard is between the true leopard and the smaller cats of the Far East. Most of these smaller cats live and hunt largely in the trees, taking anything from insects and mice to small monkeys. Because of their body size they do not need to hunt very often. Their kills tend to be rich in protein, providing enough energy to sustain them for quite a long time.

The most notable of the small cats, all of

A leopard yawns in the crook of a tree branch (left). Later it may drop on prey from above a game trail.

A smaller relative is the clouded leopard (top right); the snow leopard (bottom right) has adapted to life at up to 20,000 ft (6,096 m) and generally has a thicker coat.

which belong to the 'true cat' genus, *Felis*, include the jungle cat, *Felis chaus*, *chaus* interestingly and oddly being an ancient name for the wildcat of Africa. The jungle cat, which weighs up to 20 lb (9 kg), preys largely on birds including pheasants and jungle fowl and lives in the drier and more open forest. Then there is the fishing cat *Felis viverrina*, meaning the ferret-like cat, which frequents swampy ground, has slightly webbed feet and can, as its name suggests, hook fish out of shallow water with its claws; the flat-headed cat, *Felis plamiceps*, of Malaya, Borneo and Sumatra which preys on frogs, fish and small birds and the marbled cat, *Felis marmorata*, which lives in Sumatra and Borneo and is only slightly larger than a domestic cat.

The introduction to this book said that the Himalayas have formed an impassable barrier in the distribution of Eastern wildlife. So they have. However, this is not to say that many forms of life have not been able to adapt to life on slopes up to the 10,000-ft (3,050 m) level, and in some cases higher.

One of the true leopards has done this most successfully. The snow leopard, *Panthera uncia*, has adapted to life among the screes and snows at altitudes of up to 20,000 ft (6,100 m). It is about the same size as its jungle relative, weighing up to 100 lb (45 kg) and measuring, nose to tail, as much as 7½ ft (2.3 m). The coat is one of the most beautiful among the cats of the East. The hairs are long to protect it against the bitter alpine nights. The general colour is grey-brown with blurred black rosettes.

During the day they hunt over large territories for small rodents as well as blue sheep, tahr, the Himalayan mountain goat, the young of yaks and mountain birds such as the snowcock and blood pheasant. They range from the Himalayas right up into the Altai mountains of Mongolia. Snow leopards have the distinction of being the only true big cat of the mountains.

A yak on the lower slopes of the peak of Nuptse.
(Overleaf) Young leopards playing in water.

A LEOPARD CALLED HARRIET

Many people have kept leopards that they have hand-reared from cubs. Most will tell you that you can never entirely trust a 'tame' leopard and some have the scars to prove it.

Harriet was an exception but then she was reared by an exceptional man. Billy Arjan Singh lives at Tiger Haven on the borders of Dudwa National Park in the Indian province of Uttar Pradesh. At Dudwa the plains give way to the forests, which in turn give way to the foothills of the Himalayas. Five miles (8 km) away is India's border with Nepal.

When he came out of the forces at the end of the Second World War, Billy bought 260 acres (105 hectares) to farm at Dudwa. But it was the wildlife that really fascinated him—tiger, leopard, and their prey, the deer, the spotted chital, sambar, hog deer, swamp deer and muntjac. In the 1960s he made Tiger Haven into a wildlife sanctuary that perfectly complemented the 83 square miles (215 sq km) of Dudwa National Park, run by the Indian Forest Department, just across the river.

Billy Arjan Singh's reputation as a dedicated conservationist grew fast. So, when an orphaned leopard cub was found after her mother had been killed for her skin, the infant was brought to him in the hope that he could rear it. Billy had already hand-reared a male cub and successfully released it into the wild. Now he planned to do the same with the female cub, who had been given the most unleopard-like name of Harriet.

Billy Arjan Singh's sympathy for and understanding of big cats is possibly unique. From the start, Harriet was always trustworthy and almost overwhelmingly affectionate. When she played, charging him at full speed, she would often knock him over but always retracted her claws, which, when used for hunting in the wild, can tear a wild pig or deer apart. Harriet never even scratched him.

Dogs are high on a wild leopard's list of favourite foods. When she play-fought with Elie, Billy's mongrel dog, Harriet actually pulled her punches when unleashing swipes with her paws that could easily have crushed the dog's skull. Interestingly, Elie was top dog at Tiger Haven. Both Harriet and Tara, a young female tiger that Billy started to rear when the leopardess was three, deferred to the dog. Elie had been at Tiger Haven before they both arrived and that apparently confirmed the pecking order.

The first sign that Harriet had not lost her wild instincts came in her third year, when she left the house and started to go off hunting at night. One morning she brought back to Billy's house at Tiger Haven a young chital she had killed. Just as a wild leopard would store its prey out of the reach of scavengers and rival predators high in the branches of a tree, Harriet took her victim on to the roof out of Elie's reach.

One morning the alarm calls of

Billy Arjan Singh has an amazing rapport with big cats. Harriet is completely relaxed as he carries her (above).

Arjan Singh ferries Harriet and one of her cubs across the river to her den in the jungle (right).

grey langur monkeys alerted Bill Arjan Singh that Harriet was somewhere down by the river that forms the boundary with the National Park. Recently he had heard the rasping cough of a male leopard across the river at night. Billy was fairly sure that Harriet had not gone to the river simply to get a drink and that a stronger instinct was governing her behaviour.

Leopards are not keen on swimming. Billy could easily have ferried her across the river in his boat, as he had done many times before. But now he wanted to see what she would do if left to solve the problem herself.

After putting a trial foot several times in the river, Harriet launched herself and swam as if she had been used to water all her life.

Billy rowed across and followed her at a discreet distance. Harriet showed a keen interest in what were plainly a male leopard's calling cards, his scent marks on trees and bushes. She rubbed herself against the base of a tree as a sign that she, too, had passed that way.

After that she stayed away from Tiger Haven for days at a time. Then, one morning, just as suddenly as she had taken leave of absence, she was back. To Billy she was quite as affectionate, but as the days passed he became certain that she was pregnant.

A leopard's gestation lasts three months. At the start of the third month, Billy built Harriet a den in a tree in the forest close to Tiger Haven. He led her to it and was delighted to find that she accepted the lair at once. Towards the end of her confinement she climbed up into the den and refused to leave. She showed no objection to Billy scaling the ladder to look in. One morning when he

Harriet's cub Choti at Billy's house at Tigerhaven.

did so he found Harriet cleaning two newborn cubs. She greeted him as usual, showing not the slightest aggression. After a few days she even left the cubs for a while to give him a reassuring lick.

But wild instincts were still stirring in Harriet. Three weeks after the birth Harriet decided to move the cubs into the jungle. Possibly the tree house no longer felt safe enough. Al-most certainly she felt the need for a more natural lair. Luckily Billy saw Harriet leave, carrying the second of the cubs, and followed her at a distance. She was making for a hollow at the base of a large tree. There inside the den was the first of the cubs.

All this was unusual enough but the most extraordinary part of Billy Arjan Singh's relationship with Harriet was to come. The monsoon rains broke early that year and with exceptional force. From the shelter of Tiger Haven, Billy became increasingly worried about the fate of the cubs. The den Harriet had chosen was in an old river bed. The amount of rain that was falling made this sure to be one of the first places to flood, and though the cubs were growing fast, they were still too small to cope with flood conditions. If Harriet did not carry them to higher ground they would surely drown.

On the second day of the rising floods, Harriet appeared at Tiger Haven. She was carrying one of the cubs in her mouth. She made straight for her favourite upstairs room, the kitchen. After dropping her first cub she seemed reluctant to leave. Billy was afraid that this meant that the second cub had already drowned. He tried to calm and reassure her. But when, after an hour, the rain eased off, she quietly got up and walked out of the house.

No sooner had she crossed a small bridge near the farm than the storm resumed with even greater intensity. The river started to rise even more rapidly than before. At this rate the farm would be cut off before Harriet could return. But in an hour, with the bridge awash, Harriet was back with the second cub. For a week the leopard family stayed in the warmth of the kitchen. Then the rains eased and the river started to drop. Harriet and one of the cubs were missing.

On a hunch, Billy hurried to the river bank where he kept his boat and found Harriet waiting there. Though she had swum the river on her own, she obviously was not going to risk it with her family. Taking care not to panic her, he persuaded her to carry her cub into the boat. Then he ferried them across. As soon as the boat touched the far bank, the leopardess stepped carefully ashore with her young in her mouth. She headed away into tall grass, hid the baby and came back to the boat for the return trip to Tiger Haven.

There a strange thing happened. Instead of returning directly to the river, she made a complete tour of the upper storey of the house. It does not do to attribute human motives to animals but Billy said afterwards that it was as if she was reluctant to leave and did not expect to be back.

And so it turned out. For some days Harriet kept her cubs within easy reach of the far bank of the river. In the deep jungle beyond, her family would face all the dangers of the forest—tigers, sloth bears, even poachers—dangers with which a truly wild leopard would be better equipped to deal.

Billy Arjan Singh saw the family once or twice during the next week and then Harriet and her cubs melted away into the jungle. From time to time there were rumours that she had been killed but she certainly survived to raise another litter. It seems after all that there is no way a leopard can really change its spots when the jungle, with all its mysteries, delights and dangers, lies out there beckoning.

Harriet demonstrates an adult leopard's amazing powers of leaping.

3

LAST ROUND-UP OF

THE ELEPHANTS?

BETWEEN twenty and thirty million years ago a new sort of mammal evolved that had an unusually long nose. The nose probably started out fairly small, like that of, say, the modern tapir. The elongated nose, however, gave these animals a considerable advantage over their competitors. They were vegetarians or, to be more accurate, herbivores. The nose which they used for gathering food enabled them to pluck grass and reeds at their feet and to reach up into the trees above their heads. That nose has stood their descendants in very good stead right up until this day. Because they possessed this extraordinary proboscis, science christened them the Proboscidea.

During the millions of years since they first made their appearance, at least a hundred species of Proboscidea have come and gone. We know this from their fossil remains. Some are well known to us. Others, though recognizably elephant-like, had unfamiliar features. For instance, the *Deinotherium*, which roamed Europe some two million years ago, had downward-pointing tusks. The mammoth had a shaggy coat to protect it against the rigours of the ice ages.

The nose, or, more familiarly, trunk that these creatures developed is perhaps the most amazing and versatile organ in the entire animal kingdom. It is used for breathing, especially when swimming. It is a superbly efficient food gatherer, and can siphon ten gallons of water at a single suck and squirt this into the elephant's mouth. The trunk is powerful enough to uproot trees or tear great limbs from their upper branches. As a weapon it is formidable in the extreme. One tap from it has been known to drive the head of a human adversary down between his shoulder blades. It is used for greeting other elephants. Held vertically, it sensitively samples the wind to scent danger or find water. Its owner uses it to cool itself by squirting water or hurling dust over its body. When water is in short supply, the trunk works with a forefoot to dig a hole in a dried-out river bed until moisture is found. Having found water, which in these circumstances is bound to be tainted with sand, the elephant uses its trunk as a filtering device, swinging the tip until all the sand is thrown out and only the water is left.

A herd of Asian elephant cows with calves drink and cool themselves with mud.

Originally there were six families of these amazing trunk-owning creatures. Today five of these are extinct. Only one, the Elephantidae, remains. This present family boasts two genera, each of which contains only one species. These are known to us as the African elephant, *Loxodonta africana*, and the Asian elephant, *Elephas maximus*. The latter is closer than the African elephant to the prehistoric mammoth, which was not, incidentally, as big as most people think. It was smaller than today's African elephant. Both species have a common ancestor. Their geographical distribution took place at least two to three million years ago. The physical differences between the two species have therefore evolved within that time-scale.

In fact, the scientific name for the Asian elephant, *Elephas maximus*, is a confusing one. A fully grown adult African elephant can stand 18 in (46 cm) taller and weigh a ton (1 tonne) more than its Asian cousin, though the latter, at 5 tons (5.08 tonnes) and 10 ft (3 m) high, is impressive enough.

Height and weight are by no means the only differences. The Asian elephant has a more domed forehead with a cleft in the centre of its brow. Its back is more steeply curved. It usually has more nails on its feet than the African species. There are, however, more significant differences. The Asian elephant's ears are far smaller. Where the African species has two opposed prehensile lips or perhaps 'fingers' at the tip of its trunk, the Asian has only one on the upper surface. Even more striking, only the bulls of the Asian species carry tusks, a fact that has spared the cows from ivory poachers. Alas, for the bulls, there are very few big 'tuskers' left. They have almost all been shot for the ivory they carry, which can weigh as much as 100 lb (45 kg) a tusk. In most areas, only bulls with small ivory survive, a fact which bodes ill, genetically speaking, for the future of the species—if indeed it has any future in the wild at all.

No one can be quite sure, of course, what has caused the two species to evolve in slightly different ways. The most likely answer is to be found in the habitats they frequent. The African elephant lives mainly on grassland or wooded savanna and in light forest, though there are African elephants that live in rain forests at up to 8,000 ft (2,440 m).

The Asian elephant is basically a jungle-living animal, lying up in shade during the day and feeding mostly when it gets cool. This provides a likely explanation for the difference in size of the ears. The huge ears of the African elephant not only act as fans to cool its body but form a radiator for dissipating heat through their network of small veins. It needs this cooling device because it is more exposed to the direct heat of the sun. The forest habitat of the Asian elephant allows it more shade. It seems likely that the two 'fingers' at the tip of the trunk are more useful to a species that lives on savanna and finds much of its food by

Two young bull 'koonkies', or tame elephants, play-fighting (below). A herd of Asian elephants in woodland savanna (right).

A price on his head? One of the few remaining big tuskers in Assam (left). A big male with crossed tusks (above). The brown patch on his head is a mud pack used for cooling or to deter parasites.

grazing. The single 'finger' of the Asiatic species is highly suitable for feeding in a jungle habitat. The other main difference between the two species is far more difficult to explain. Why only bull Asian elephants carry tusks remains a mystery.

The sad story of the decline of the African elephant mainly due to ivory poaching has received a great deal of much-needed publicity. In purely numerical terms, the Asian elephant is in even greater trouble, though its plight is less well known.

In 1973 the Fauna and Flora Preservation Society of London sponsored a comprehensive survey of the Asian elephant, one of the most important aspects of which was an attempt to take a census of the population still remaining in the wild. In 1978 Robert Olivier, Co-Chairman of the Survival Service Commission's Asian Elephant Group, came up with an estimated figure of between 28,000 and 40,000 elephants. If this seems a great many elephants, just consider the area over which they are spread. It reaches from Bangladesh to China. After five years' work, Olivier was certain of only two things: that the population, even at the highest estimate, was by no means enough to ensure the eventual survival of the species; and that the figures henceforward would be on the way down rather than up. In the thirteen years since, there is little doubt that the total has decreased considerably.

In the fairly recent zoological past, around 2500 BC, the range of the Asian elephant reached from the Tigris–Euphrates basin to China, at least as far north as the River Yangtze. The first populations to go were those of western Asia. The first record of elephants in what used to be called Assyria is dated 1700 BC. There was then a regular trade in ivory from this source between Egypt and the western Mediterranean countries. The Egyptians, who conquered western Asia in the fifteenth century BC, hunted there, having recently wiped out the last elephants in their own lands. This gave a measure of protection since the Pharaohs wanted to preserve some animals to hunt. The last hunt took place in the ninth century BC, after which the ivory trade was resumed with the inevitable result. Several centuries before Christ, the Asian elephant had disappeared from western Asia. Even so, it seems that the species survived in the Tigris–Euphrates basin longer than it did in the vast area between there and the Punjab. The eastward retreat of the species has been a steady, relentless process ever since. The writers of the Mogul era of Indian rule recorded this fact as early as the fifteenth century.

Despite the damage man has done to the Asian elephant, he has long had a close part-

A carving of an Asian elephant on a temple wall at Kandy, Sri Lanka.

nership with the great animal founded if not on love then certainly on respect.

The earliest records of elephants being tamed for work and ceremonial duties occur on carvings that have been dated not later than 2500 BC, from Mohenjo-Daro on the lower Indus. The elephant–man relationship is an incredible one. It is quite easy to imagine how early man struck up a working partnership with the dog. It probably began when jackals huddled round his camp-fire to snatch bones and scraps of food. From that it was just a short step to encouraging the animals to help him hunt, no doubt a piece of teamwork from which both benefited. But to tame an animal as awe-inspiring as a wild elephant, to make it work in the forests and to carry man into battle! Robert Olivier suggests that the first tame elephants may have been orphaned calves reared as pets. These captives may even have been used to lure and help catch wild elephants of which there were then a great number. The cultural relationship with the elephant grew fast and became part of Eastern mythology, religion, warfare and day-to-day working life.

In the days of the Mogul rule in India, it was common for an emperor to have 1,500 war elephants at his command. The emperor Jahangir, who ruled in the fifteenth century, was said to have 12,000 war elephants in his personal army and over 40,000 in his entire kingdom. The num-

bers of tame elephants kept at any one time between the eleventh and seventeenth centuries certainly exceeded the entire wild population left in the world today!

In many parts of the Asian elephants' range the slaughter began with the coming of colonial man, who not only shot for sport but also cleared the forest for rubber and other crops and naturally did not want elephants to undo his good work. Even so there were still more than enough elephants to guarantee the safety of the species. The decline in numbers did not really set in until after the Second World War, when elephants were, incidentally, used to carry ammunition during the Burma campaign.

The trend accelerated greatly with the coming of Independence to India in 1947 and then to other countries of the Far East. Hydroelectric schemes and dams, sometimes ill-conceived and subsequently damaging to the environment; roads and cultivation; forest clearance, often to make a quick profit: all these and many more 'improvements' drove the elephant into areas where it had never lived before. And as more and more of these areas were given over to cultivation, crop-raiding increased and so did the toll of human lives. Crop-protection guns were issued wholesale, the users of which as often wounded elephants as killed them outright, so that the surviving animals became even more dangerous. It is easy to be critical. It has to be remembered that India and many countries of the Far East had appalling economic and social problems, not the least of which was providing food for their expanding populations. Elephant conservation was not a top priority, nor was the sort of environmental planning that takes into consideration the needs of wildlife as well as those of humans. Indeed, even in 1991 there is little real evidence of such planning by governments and industry. The result of all this is that the Asian elephant is for the most part now confined to hilly and mountainous regions. These tend to resist human development the longest but will in the end, no doubt, succumb to the all-conquering technology of the world's dominant species, *Homo sapiens.*

(Previous page) The epitome of joy for a tame elephant – water, and plenty of it, at the end of a working day.

A working elephant carries its own fuel – leaves for the evening meal.

For the record, Olivier's 1978 elephant census came up with the following figures:

Indian subcontinent (India, Nepal, Bhutan, Bangladesh): 9,950-15,050

Continental South-East Asia: 11,000-14,600

Burma: 5,000
China: 100
Thailand: 2,500-4,500
Kampuchea, Laos, Vietnam: 3,500-5,000

Island and Peninsular South-East Asia: 7,330-12,330

Andaman Islands: 30
Borneo: 2,000
Malaya: 3,000-6,000
Sri Lanka: 2,000-4,000
Sumatra: 300

These estimates add up to the figures quoted earlier, namely between 28,000 and 40,000 wild Asian elephants scattered over an immense area. On the basis of this admittedly approximate but certainly not over-optimistic census, the Asian elephant was officially declared an endangered species.

THE LAST ROUND-UP

Most people believe that the Asian elephant is the only one that can be tamed and trained, that the African species is far too wild and dangerous. This is no doubt reinforced by the fact that the Asian elephant is the species always seen in circuses.

The facts do not confirm this belief. Before the Second World War there was a successful training centre for African elephants in what was then the Belgian Congo but is now Zaïre. The elephants were trained for forest work.

Again, anyone like Daphne Sheldrick, who wrote *The Orphans of Tsavo* about the wild animals she reared in Tsavo National Park, Kenya, where her husband David was for many years the highly successful warden, knows that African elephant calves are easily tamed. Though as sub-adults her orphans spent their days in the bush, they remained completely trustworthy and almost affectionate with her, and her African helpers. There is, it seems, absolutely no reason why *Loxodonta africana* should not be tamed and trained as readily as *Elephas maximus*. The difference is mainly one of need and opportunity.

In Asia there are many more forests in which the elephant with its enormous strength and lifting power has proved an invaluable aid. Society in India and the Far East generally was historically far more formal and organized than were the tribal systems of Africa. Thus trained elephants could play a vital part in armies. It

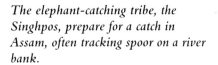

The elephant-catching tribe, the Singhpos, prepare for a catch in Assam, often tracking spoor on a river bank.

might be said that war elephants were the battle tanks of the Moguls. Religion was highly developed and ritualized. A beautifully caparisoned elephant makes the most impressive addition to a state or religious occasion (see page 110).

In the not-so-distant past the major centres for the capture and trade of local wild elephants were in Bengal, Ceylon and Pegu in Burma. These centres received elephants from other areas for training. In the eighteenth century there was a substantial Far Eastern trade in trained elephants. Madras, for example, imported them from as far away as Ceylon and Malaya. In those days there was no shortage of wild stocks on which to draw. Today, though trapping still goes on, it is disappearing because there are not enough wild elephants to justify it. Now that

the Asian elephant has been put on the endangered list and included in the Red Data Book of the International Union for the Conservation of Nature's Survival Service, governments will find it difficult officially to sanction catching operations. One of the last of these for which permission was formally given took place in Assam, the north-east province of India where there is still a reasonable elephant population.

What may well prove to be India's last round-up of wild elephants was carried out by a tribe who have specialized in elephant catching and training for centuries. The tribe are called the Singphos (pronounced Sing-po). The methods they use, the *mela shikar* and the *khedda*, have not altered for thousands of years.

Khedda means stockade. Before the catching can start, the *khedda* has to

Ordeal by fire and song – an early stage in the training of captured elephants.

be built. For this the Singphos, whose traditional uniform is a kind of striped jacket, use their trained elephants called *koonkies*. The *koonkies* carry the tree trunks that will form the walls of the stockade and can even break off a branch to the required length with their feet if commanded to do so. The trained females who have calves at foot keep their young with them as they work.

When reconnaissance shows that there is a large herd of elephants with young calves close to camp it is often decided to try to capture some of the young elephants first by means of *mela shikar*. Like everything else in elephant capture, this is a hazardous operation and would be impossible but for the presence of the trained *koonkies*.

Using hand-woven ropes—the Singphos do not trust any catching gear they have not made themselves —they ride their trained elephants right in among the herd. Amazingly the wild elephants accept the *koonkies* even though the catchers are on their backs and despite the fact that the herd is being chased by them. The aim is to separate a calf and lasso it. This is the time of maximum danger when the mother and attendant adults may decide to charge. When everything goes well the captive, securely roped and sandwiched between two tame elephants, is led back to camp without serious difficulty. It is not always as easy as that; nor can adults be caught with the *mela*. For them the *khedda* is called for.

The *khedda* looks too flimsy to hold a herd of furious, newly rounded-up elephants but that is exactly what it is designed to do. The branches that form the walls are light and springy but they are backed by stout tree trunks. The principle is that the stockade will give but not break.

Timing is all-important with the *khedda*. The drive starts in late afternoon so that as the light is beginning to fade the herd will be driven into the log walls that funnel into the stockade. The key part in the drive is once again played by the trained elephants. They are reinforced by beaters on foot banging drums and gongs. The only modern touch is the use of the occasional thunderflash to keep the wild herd on the move in the right direction.

It is dusk by the time the wild elephants reach the funnel and now the noise of the beaters behind them is so loud that they simply keep going—into the *khedda*. As it grows dark, fires are lit all around the stockade. Without this intimidating ring of fire the herd might easily smash its way out.

Next morning the Singphos are exhausted, but not the captured elephants. With daylight and without the restraint of the fires outside the walls, they are more restive than ever. Now there is a real danger of a breakout. So the head catcher decides that the moment has come to go in and bring the captives out, starting with the calves. In the confusion and stampede that is bound to occur, the young elephants may easily get trampled or crushed.

The Singphos ride in among the angry herd on their tame elephants, relying on the fact that, as in the *mela shikar*, the wild elephants will accept the *koonkies* as one of them and take no notice of the men precariously perched on their backs.

Thousands of years of experience have proved that this is what the wild elephants do—usually—though there is always a chance that it may be fatally different. First a cow is pushed out of the way by the trained elephants so that her calf can be safely roped and led away. One by one, calves and adults are given the same treatment. It is 8 miles (13 km) to the training camp. Tethered like a chain

A recently caught calf touches the 'koonkie' for reassurance.

A tricky moment in the 'khedda'. The calves must be roped and led out of the stockade first, lest the terrified adults trample them to death. Here they huddle together for comfort in their unaccustomed surroundings.

gang, the herd is led away between *koonkies*. The captives go quietly. It is almost as if they had never been wild elephants—but only the day before yesterday, they were.

The initial stages of training are not exactly kind but there is no other way of breaking a fully grown elephant. The tame elephants manoeuvre a captive into position, acting rather like gaolers. It is securely tied to tree trunks by the front feet. It is tied in such a way that no damage will result no matter how the elephant strains at its bonds. At the very least, the catchers are not going to mark with rope burns an animal that, when broken, will be worth nearly £1,000.

The captives must now be persuaded to accept man. They will never do this if they are running around loose. So the first two days must be spent tethered in solitary confinement. Often, during this time, prospective buyers come to inspect the Singphos' captures.

After a few days comes the next crucial stage in the breaking process. It takes place at night and might almost be called ordeal by fire. Fires are lit once again to subdue and intimidate the elephants. It could also be called ordeal by song, though the traditional and somewhat discordant songs sung by the trainers are said to have a soothing effect. Under the influence of song and fire, the elephants get used to being touched by their trainers and to being tapped lightly with a stick.

After that they can be taken out on the parade ground in daylight to learn the basic commands that their mahouts give them. To see that they obey, they are flanked on either side by a *koonkie* who acts as schoolmaster. The mahout, as he gives a command, reinforces the order with leg pressure just as if riding a horse.

The basic training is amazingly quick. Six months after capture the elephants will be working in the forests for their new owners, easily moving logs of several tons.

It is impossible to say whether Asian elephants enjoy working. They appear to do so. It probably depends on the mahout who rides and works them. Most mahouts, though sadly not all, value their elephants too highly to ill-treat them.

It seems certain that there is still a place for working elephants in mountainous regions where machinery cannot easily operate. Elephants are cheaper than machines, too, and do not cost so much to run. Nor do they contribute to environmental pollution by burning fossil fuels. Their fuel is all around them. It grows on trees. And they need very little maintenance and no spare parts.

Conservationists tend to take a liberal view of working elephants if only because their very existence depends on there being a healthy enough stock in the wild. Tame Asian working elephants breed readily in captivity yet their calves are usually sold off to zoos and collectors. There are two reasons for this: it would take far

too long for the calves to reach working age, and their mothers would be off work while rearing very young calves. The trade of elephant catching and training is likely to die out in the very near future. When it does, a large part of Indian folklore and tradition, sadly, will die with it.

Care and maintenance of a very large 'koonkie'. A mahout washes down his charge.

4

ISLAND OF

TWO MONSOONS

SRI Lanka hangs from the south-east tip of the Indian subcontinent like a gigantic uncut diamond. Sometime in the not-so-distant geological past, perhaps as little as half a million years ago, it was joined to the great land mass to the north. Ice ages came and went. The seas rose and fell. At times there existed a land bridge to the island. When the ice at last melted and the seas rose, Sri Lanka had not only drifted apart from its parent India, it had become cut off by an ocean gap of approximately 20 miles (32 km). A number of large mammals from India had by then caught the boat. They included the leopard, several species of deer and monkeys and the sloth bear. The tiger never managed to clamber aboard, probably because its migration through India had not yet led it far enough south.

One theory has it that the island was long ago to the west of its present position and that its north–south axis then lay in a more north-easterly direction. If this was the case, then its great central mountain massif would have formed the end of India's Western Ghats. Its flat northern half would have connected with the Carnatic plain of southern India.

How was it severed? Tectonic plate movement may well have split the Ghat, cutting off Sri Lanka from what is now Travancore. As the gap slowly widened, a mass of land drifted eastward, forming first a peninsula and then an island. G. M. Henry, in his classic *A Guide to the Birds of Ceylon*, puts forward this argument to explain why the birds that have developed as separate species and subspecies are found in the southern, mountainous half of the island. If the island did become detached in the way he suggests, then the mountainous regions in the south would have been separated far longer than the northern parts. The longer period of separation would have given time for the birds there to evolve as separate species and to have lost all connection with their original parent stock in India.

Romantically but not altogether inaccurately, James Emerson Tennant, Colonial Secretary to Ceylon, wrote of the island in 1859 in his book *Ceylon*: 'a pendant that nestles gently on the swelling bosom of the Indian Ocean. Caressed by warm waters, 770 miles [1,240 km] of golden sand ring the island. Within these sands is green, lush-green fertile land sculptured towards the centre

into soaring mountains. An emerald, fringed by filigreed gold and set in aquamarine—truly a jewelled pendant.'

In the ten years since the author spent some time making films about the rich animal life of Sri Lanka for the 'Survival' series of documentaries, that pendant has, alas, been ripped from its setting. Wars are almost as disastrous for wildlife as they are for humans. At the moment of writing, there is a bitter struggle with the 'Tamil Tigers', who demand a separate state and self-government in the northern half of the island. Many wildlife reserves and parks are too dangerous for park rangers, let alone tourists. Their very wildness provides ideal shelter in which guerrillas can hide and from which to launch attacks.

The romantic description quoted above, the 'jewel in an aquamarine sea', needs a little down-to-earth explanation. Tennant's sculptured central mountain mass needs no embellishment. The mountains are at least as beautiful as he suggests. Their slopes grow some of the finest tea in the world. Sri Pada, Adam's Peak, rises to 7,362 ft (2,244 m). At its summit is a boulder with a hollow resembling the imprint of a man's foot. The Buddhists believe that the print was made by Buddha during one of his few personal appearances. For the Hindus, the footprint commemorates the Dance of Creation of the god Siva. The Muslims believe that the spot marks Adam's punishment for disobedience and that here he was made to stand on one foot for a very long time. The British colonists, though respecting these beliefs, were more practical about Sri Lanka's mountains. They saw them as fertile slopes on which to grow tea and coffee, as well as a cool and pleasant place to live when it became uncomfortably hot nearer sea level.

For the large mammals, clearing the mountainsides for planting was inevitably disastrous. Elephants, leopard, deer and bear were either shot or forced to move to the lowlands, which the colonists did not particularly covet. Their surviving descendants remain there to this day. One hundred years ago there were 12,000 elephants in an island just 130 miles (209 km) wide and 270

miles (434 km) long. That may even have been an underestimate since the count was made mainly in the dry, lowland areas whereas numbers of elephants may still have existed in undeveloped parts of the central mountain massif. Before the present conflict there were thought to be as many as 4,000 elephants in Sri Lanka, though 3,000 is a more likely total. Since the Tamil insurrection it is almost certain that a number have been shot for food by the 'Tigers'. Numbers of large mammals, including elephants, will have fallen victim to booby traps and land-mines.

The central mountains of the island have a far-reaching natural effect not only on the lives of its human inhabitants but also on its flora and fauna.

Thanks to the cloud-buffering action of the mountain range, Sri Lanka has two monsoons. The north-east monsoon sets in during October. The mountains cause it to drop its rain on the east side of the island until January. The south-west monsoon arrives in April and brings rain to the south and west of the island until September, with May the wettest month of all. But the south and west also receive a fair amount of rain from the north-east monsoon. As a result, the south-west of Sri Lanka has an annual rainfall of 80-200 in (200-510 cm). The north-east parts have to make do with anything from 25 to 75 in (65-190 cm) annually.

The great lake in Gol-Oya National Park, Sri Lanka, formed by flooding of the valley, contains many bare tree stumps, killed by the rising water (previous page and left).

Monsoon storm clouds gather at Gol-Oya. Seasonally the lake rises dramatically.

Thanks to its central mountain range, Sri Lanka has two monsoons: the North-East monsoon sets in during October, the South-West monsoon in April.

Painted storks nest around Sri Lanka's many lakes and 'villus'.

Meteorologists split the island into two climatic areas. The Dry Zone covers most of the northern end of the island and the entire eastern half; the Wet Zone, the south-west corner, where rain can fall almost any week of the year.

Though the mammals can cope with conditions in either zone, the flora and the bird life are largely governed by the effect the central mountains have on the rainfall. Vegetation in the driest parts of the north-western coastal area is of a semi-desert type. The birds in the Dry Zone tend to be more specialized. Strangely enough, water birds are most abundant in the Dry Zone. One reason is that there are several very large lakes and reservoirs for roosting and feeding and these provide nesting cover and plenty of aquatic food and insect life for the young.

Kumana *villu*—*villu* means lake—is the finest waterbird lagoon on the dry south-eastern coast. It is part of Yala National Park. Most of the lakes in the park dry up since they rely on the north-east monsoon. The water it brings does not last the year round. Kumana is different. Not only is it close to the coast but also to a large river, the Kumbukan. In the dry season, when the flow of the river is less powerful, wave action from the sea builds up a sand bar at its mouth, blocking its exit. This natural dam ensures that, even during the driest part of the year, the river level stays high. A side channel from the estuary leads to Kumana lake and keeps it full when the *villus* elsewhere are dry. The migrant water birds come to Kumana in April. The *villu* includes mangroves on the seaward side and tall *kirala* trees on the banks and islands of the freshwater lagoon. These provide nesting cover for the larger birds such as the painted storks, spotted-billed pelicans, spoonbills, white ibises, open-bill storks, four species of heron, three egret species, the chestnut bittern, the Indian darter, little cormorants and Indian shags. In the *karang* bushes, whistling teal and water hens nest just above water level.

But possibly the most fascinating of Kumana's birds nests on the water itself. The almost constant level of the lagoon means that large beds of lotus plants, the water lily with the delicate purple flower, cover the surface. These leaves provide the lily-trotter, or jacana, with a unique floating home.

Jacanas live in many tropical countries but only one species, perhaps the most beautiful of all, is found in Sri Lanka. The pheasant-tailed jacana seems to walk on the water. In fact, all jacanas can perform this trick. Their secret lies in their enormously elongated toes, which spread their weight over a wide area of lily leaf. The floating lily platform provides the jacanas with all their needs—shelter, nesting sites and an ample year-round supply of aquatic insects, molluscs and seeds.

The jacanas are resident at Kumana and start to nest in February before the migrants arrive. Their nesting system is an extremely unusual one. The females play a dominant role, marking out for themselves a large territory on the lotus beds. Within this area, several males—smaller and less gaudy than the females—establish much smaller

---

A black-crowned night heron, distributed the world over and common in Sri Lanka.

(Overleaf) Birds that walk, live and nest on water. Two pheasant-tailed jacana chicks and eggs on a lily pad nest.

The male pheasant-tailed jacana takes over once the eggs are laid and broods them, leaving the hen free to lay again in other nests in her territory.

A great white heron uses a water buffalo as a fishing perch.

or wedge-shaped: narrow at one end and broad at the other. To protect them against immersion, they have a waterproof coating.

When the female has laid, the male takes over. He does all the brooding, leaving the female free to mate and lay in all the other nests within her territory. A female jacana can lay up to eight clutches of eggs, each one in a different male's nest. This form of role-reversal is known as polyandry, a term applied to a woman who has more than one husband.

The lily pads are a dangerous place for the young jacana chicks as the lake is full of predators that prey on eggs and chicks—fish, lizards, snakes, young crocodiles as well as predatory birds. The chicks are not likely to drown as they can conceal themselves underwater for up to twenty minutes. The ability of the female to leave the brooding of the eggs to the male while she moves on to lay more clutches elsewhere is another obvious advantage to the species.

The male has his own repertoire of survival tricks to protect the brood. If one nest is threatened he will often roll the eggs, one at a time, for quite long distances across the lily leaves until he reaches a reserve nest built for just such an emergency.

The eggs hatch in twenty-six days, and the chicks are able to stand and walk almost immediately they emerge. The male does nothing to feed them and from the start they find all their food for themselves. But he does give them shelter if danger threatens. If a hawk flies over or a snake appears, he lets the young hop up under his wing and lifts them off the lily pads so that only their legs can be seen hanging down. At six weeks, the young jacanas are independent and almost fully grown, though they will not acquire their fine adult plumage and be ready to breed until they are two.

In July the north-east monsoon arrives at Kumana. By then the breeding season is well over. Territorial squabbles are forgotten and the jacanas form into large flocks. The Kumbukan river rises with the first rains and breaks down the sand bar between itself and the sea. But the

territories. Both sexes defend their chosen areas against rivals. If a female disputes territory with another hen bird, the male does not intervene, but stands meekly by.

As each cock jacana establishes his territory he starts to build a simple platform of floating vegetation. These nests will shortly be visited by the female in whose larger territory the various males have set up home. Once the nest is ready, the male attracts the female with a sort of 'ticking' call. Soon after mating, the first egg is laid. Three more follow at daily intervals. Once she has deposited her clutch in the nest the female has no further interest in it or her eggs. To prevent them rolling off into the water, the eggs are cuneiform,

monsoon rain will provide enough water to keep Kumana *villu* full and the lotus pads flourishing until the dry season comes round and the jacanas and all the other water birds are ready to start nesting again.

Kumana is a natural water reserve. Gol-Oya, 40 miles (64 km) to the north is man-made but none the less spectacular for that. In 1950, a dam was thrown across the Gol-Oya river forming a lake of 35 square miles (91 sq km), the Senanayaka Samudra. In Sri Lanka artificial reservoirs, re-gardless of size, are called 'tanks'. This is a very large tank indeed, a place of great natural beauty and the centrepiece of Gol-Oya National Park. Attracted by an endless supply of water, large herds of elephants have moved into the park, as well as wild water buffalo, sambar and chital deer. The western hills of this park of 90 square miles

Cattle egret in full breeding plumage at Kumana (above).

Gol-Oya Lake is the finest place in the East to watch white-bellied sea eagles swooping on fish (right).

(233 sq km) are the home of the rare painted partridge, and of bush quail and jungle fowl.

It is, however, the great lake itself that domi-nates the scene, with its forests of dead trees, bare

The head of a master angler – the white-bellied sea eagle is a close relative of America's national emblem, the bald eagle.

trunks standing tall out of the water like the masts of a vast fleet at anchor. These bare poles are all that remains of the jungle that the lake drowned as the waters rose behind the dam. Swimming among the flooded trees are great rafts of cormorants, often 5,000 strong. Cormorants are only there for one reason: the lake is filled with fish. It is these that attract the star performer of Gol-Oya: the white-bellied sea eagle.

This bird is a close relative of the African fish eagle and America's national emblem, the bald eagle. All survive by catching fish. The sea eagle, with its light grey and white plumage and black-tipped primaries, is arguably the most handsome of the *Haliaeëtus* genus to which all three fish-catchers belong. It is not exclusive to Sri Lanka. Its range includes the coasts of China and India and as far south as the shore of Australia and Tasmania. But there is no finer place than Gol-Oya to see numbers of these great birds in action catching fish and performing aerial courtship displays in the breeding season.

Soon after the valley was dammed, tilapia were introduced as a food fish. The lake grows fish as prolifically as its bed once grew the trees of a dense jungle. Fishermen, cormorants and sea eagles were not slow to discover this fact. The lake is commercially netted by licensed fishermen. Netting always produces a number of damaged fish, which come to the surface dead or dying, and these provide easy prey for the eagles and cormorants. The eagle, however, is quite capable of catching live fish weighing up to 3 lb (1.4 kg) if they are careless enough to bask near the surface. Fishing eagles either use the trees around the lake edge as lookout points or soar high above the lake watching for the tell-tale dorsal fin of a basking tilapia to break the surface. The birds can spot their targets from half a mile (0.8 km). The attack is a low-level one, the hooked talons thrown forward at the last moment to seize the fish, the forward speed of the eagle pulling the catch from the water.

The white-bellied sea eagle's breeding season at Gol-Oya starts with the end of the monsoon in February and March. The nests are often built 50 ft (15 m) up the tallest trees and are used year after year. The untidy pile of sticks is repaired and added to. When there are young in the nest—the clutch is usually two—the eagles have to catch fish at least twice a day. The young eagles are ready to leave the nest after just over two months but are not ready to breed until they are three years old. Long before then the adults will have driven them out of their own territories and probably away from Gol-Oya altogether.

'Land of the Lakes' is what Wilpattu means. Wilpattu is the largest of Sri Lanka's National parks, sprawling across the north-west section of the island and covering 500 square miles (1,295 sq km).

The lakes are certainly there but they are hidden in dense jungle, only accessible by a network of sandy tracks. Without the *villus* a visitor would see very little in Wilpattu, though occasionally a day-hunting leopard will step out on the road, or a sloth bear stand 6 ft (1.8 m) high as it reaches for the fruit, honey or tree termites on which these fierce-looking predators feed. Sloth bears have a bad reputation for attacking villagers which is occasionally merited. In the main they are shy creatures, though their speed, strength and agility demand a healthy respect. Even leopards sometimes come off second-best in a fight with one.

Although you might not meet an elephant on the Wilpattu jungle tracks, you know that they are there when you find a tree pulled down or bull-dozed across the road. The *villus*, which are usually surrounded by a circular, sandy, open space, look as though the jungle at this point was cleared by some vanished forest people. They are, in fact, natural formations. When the monsoon rains fill the *villus*, their waters reach almost to the jungle edge. It is this annual flooding that prevents jungle growth from recolonizing the open space that surrounds the water.

Wait patiently and long enough at the start and the end of the day at different *villus* and you will see or hear most of Sri Lanka's wildlife. When the *villu* is full, the reedy margins attract a great many wading birds such as the Ceylon black-winged stilt which, like many of the island's 380 birds, is a unique subspecies. The water attracts migrants from Siberia, such as the Asiatic golden plover and the greenshank. The noisiest of waders, the red-wattled lapwings, nest in the rough grass around the water's edge and 'buzz' every intruder from a terrapin, finding its way to the water, to a wild pig. Their aerial attack is accompanied by a machine-gun burst of their screaming, irritating cry, sometimes transcribed as an endlessly repeated *did-he-do-it?*

Wild water buffalos come to drink at the *villus*, where their calves run the risk of being snatched by the jaws of a large mugger, the marsh crocodile of the Far East. As far as humans are concerned, the mugger is the least aggressive of the crocodilians. The most cautious drinkers are the deer, the spotted chital, the skulking muntjac or barking deer, and the heavyweight sambar. They know that they are prime leopard prey and that the leopards regularly hunt the *villus*.

Red jungle fowl, the ancestors of all our domestic chickens, sun themselves on the edge of the forest. Peacocks or, to be more correct, Indian peafowl males, fan their many-eyed tails in display not only at peahens but at almost any creature that passes.

In 1983, Wilpattu was on the receiving end of one of the most dramatic wildlife rescue operations in the history of conservation. The story begins at a place called Deduru-Oya some 50 miles (80 km) distant.

Probably the greatest dandy in the world of birds, the male Indian peafowl (left). Despite their elaborate plumage, peafowl are competent fliers and can frequently be seen in trees (right). Reverse angle on a male peacock in full display (below).

(Overleaf) Beauty is in the eye of the beheld. The colouring in the peacock's tail feathers is not pigment but a reflecting material that changes colour as the light strikes it.

The mugger, the freshwater crocodile of India and Sri Lanka, is not dangerous to humans, though it will catch deer, wild pig and pythons.

As pressure for land grows, more and more of Sri Lanka's surviving elephants find themselves cut off in small patches of forest surrounded by agriculture. These isolated elephant communities are known as 'pocketed herds'.

The jungle in which they are isolated provides them with shelter but cannot possibly offer them enough food. An elephant needs around 600 lb (270 kg) of vegetation a day. Food is to be found on the farmland all around and so the herds help themselves. The local people naturally defend their crops, usually with totally inadequate weapons such as ancient shotguns loaded with buckshot. A wounded elephant is a dangerous elephant. Farmers are killed and so the problem escalates. One such pocketed herd lived in a small patch of jungle in the centre of a coconut-growing area at Deduru-Oya.

The herd had once consisted of 150 animals. Now it was reduced to seventeen. The Wildlife Department had tried to rescue a similar herd some ten years before at a place called Uda Wal-awe. The attempt was not a success. Because of the thickness of the scrub, bulldozers were used to carry the warden using the tranquillizing dart gun within range. Three adult bulls were captured. One had to be destroyed because it was too dangerous to handle. The other two died within three weeks, presumably from stress. Although a few other animals were captured, no adults were successfully moved out of the danger area. The conclusion was that it would be better to destroy the larger animals humanely than to attempt to move them to a safer place.

The approach at Deduru-Oya was quite different. Lyn de Alwis, Director of the Sri Lanka National Parks, had a secret weapon, although it is debatable whether you can call a facility that has been in existence for several thousand years

105

'secret'. An earlier chapter (see page 77) describes how the *koonkies*, the trained elephants of the Singpho elephant catchers in Assam, lull wild elephants into a feeling of security after capture. Lyn de Alwis now proposed to use the same technique to persuade captured wild elephants to walk quietly into the back of a truck. There was, however, one big difference. The captives in this case would be under the influence of tranquillizing drugs.

De Alwis, Dr Netasinghe, head of the veterinary team, and the park rangers and trackers had another trump card in the person of the man who was to carry out the darting. Ian Hofmeyr, veterinary officer of Etosha National Park, Namibia, was one of the most experienced capture officers in Africa. Hofmeyr had volunteered his services free of charge. Though the jungle at Deduru-Oya was as thick as that at Uda Walawe, there would be no question of darting from a bulldozer. This time the stalk would be on foot so that the dart could be placed accurately and to maximum effect. This meant approaching highly unpredictable, often wounded elephants, in dense undergrowth at a range of 15 yards (14 m). It was about as dangerous as any darting operation can be, but the Sri Lankan trackers readily volunteered to go with Hofmeyr.

There were no accidents unless you count 'Survival' wildlife cameraman Dieter Plage being run down by an enraged tusker who passed right over him as he lay on the ground. One great foot actually touched his shirt as he lay under the charging animal with his camera still running! Of the ten animals successfully darted, nine had buckshot or bullet wounds. One bull was blind in both eyes.

Now came the part of the operation that would have been impossible without the trained elephants. Each captive was injected with a tranquillizer. A trained work elephant then moved up on either side, rather like tugs docking a ship. At first the difficulty was with the mahouts rather than the *koonkies*. Experienced as these riders were, they could not believe that the drugs would make the captives docile. Gradually their confi-

dence increased. When each captive reached the loading ramp leading to the back of the truck, it walked calmly aboard guided by its escorts. Ropes were then put on to keep it there but these alone certainly could not have restrained a 5-ton (5.08 tonnes) elephant if it had taken it into its head to dismount during the journey. The drive to Wilpattu takes from three to five hours, depending on weather conditions. Since it was the start of the monsoon they drove through torrential downpours which the elephants, if not the drivers, thoroughly enjoyed. During the journey, frequent stops were made to check the loads and inject booster shots of tranquillizers into the elephants.

The first release in Wilpattu was made at night to reduce the risk of the elephant straying in strange surroundings. A large '1' was painted on the elephant's backside for future identification purposes. Hofmeyr gave the elephant a small shot of tranquillizer. Handlers guided it down the ramp with ropes and then let it wander away rather unsteadily. Ten adult elephants—each with a number painted on it—were successfully moved and released in this fashion. All stayed in the park except Number 10, an adult cow. She walked back 50 miles (80 km) across country in four days to the forest at Deduru-Oya, where Ian Hofmeyr had darted her. Ian was still looking for surviving elephants when she arrived back. She met him on a forest track, ran him down and did her best to kill him. Hofmeyr believed he knew why she acted like this. When captured she had a calf at foot. The calf was in such bad condition that it was decided that its only chance of survival was to transfer it to Colombo Zoo for treatment. Hofmeyr was certain that the mother had returned to look for her calf and associated him with its disappearance.

★   ★   ★

A postscript must be added to this story. Indeed, it applies to most of the wildlife of Sri Lanka and its National Parks. Shortly after the Tamil uprising, a raiding party of 'Tigers' invaded Wilpattu and

without apparent reason shot all the rangers. The tracker who had worked with Ian Hofmeyr darting the Deduru-Oya elephants was forced to guide the raiders out of the park. When they reached the main gate, the Tamil Tigers shot him and threw his body out on the road.

At the moment of writing in early 1991, Kumana, Gol-Oya and Wilpattu are no-go areas owing to guerrilla activity. Rangers have been shot and no one has an accurate picture of what has happened to the wildlife there. Much obviously will have survived, but large mammals have probably been greatly reduced in number. Yala National Park in the far south-east can still be visited. Even when peace is restored, it will take a long time to get the parks operating normally again.

One of Sri Lanka's few large bull elephants on the seashore at Yala National Park.

(Overleaf) Whistling teal, or tree duck, and their brood of chicks apparently sail into the jaws of death. The mugger takes no notice.

Shortly after returning to Etosha, Ian Hofmeyr was killed when his catching truck, pulling over to make way for a lorry on a park track, rolled onto its side in an irrigation ditch. He was thrown out and killed instantly.

PEREHERA—PROCESSION OF LIGHTS

Perehera simply means procession. The Kandy Esala Perehera must be the most spectacular procession in the world.

Kandy was the ancient capital of Sri Lanka and might still be called the capital of the high country of the island. The city was the centre of the battles fought against the Sinhalese by foreign invaders in the seventeenth and eighteenth centuries. The Portuguese who ruled the coastal areas of the island captured it from the King of Kandy three times between 1505 and 1656. And it was captured once by the Dutch, who followed as would-be colonists between 1656 and 1796. Each time Kandy was held by the invaders for only a short period. It finally fell to the British in 1815.

The religious traditions of the city survived all invasions. To the Buddhists of the island it is the home of the Temple of the Tooth. The octagonal shrine, the Dalada Maligawa, houses the tooth-relic of Buddha, an object of veneration for Buddhists the world over. Tradition has it that at the cremation of Gautama Buddha in India in 543 BC the tooth survived the flames and was brought to Kandy in the fourth century AD.

The relic rests in a casket called a *karanduwa* on a silver table in the temple. Each morning temple drummers beat a tattoo to mark the passing of another stage in a year-long ritual that has been followed for more than a thousand years. As the drums beat, long lines of pilgrims dressed in white and carrying pink lotus blossoms and white frangipani file past the casket.

The relic is not on view except on special occasions and the greatest of these is the Kandy perehera in the lunar month of Esala in the Buddhist calendar. This falls in late July or early August.

The history of the perehera goes back to the second century AD, when King Gajabuha won a great victory against his foes in southern India, the Tamils, chasing them back across the narrow strait into their homeland. The king ordered a grand victory parade dedicated to the island's Hindu deities, Natha, Vishnu and Kataragama. He also introduced the cult of Pattini, another Hindu goddess. Much later, the perehera was adopted by the Buddhists to display their most sacred relic. The Kandy perehera has become a highlight of religious life throughout the island.

The perehera is unlike any other religious ritual in the world because its procession includes up to 100 elephants. And such elephants! These great beasts are given a temporary respite from their working lives to parade each day for a week through the streets of Kandy attended by drummers and dancers, the procession starting each day from a different temple.

The culmination comes on the night of the full moon when the sacred tooth of Buddha is carried through the streets of Kandy in a shrine set on top of a gigantic tusker.

A richly caparisoned elephant carries sacred temple records in the Kandy perehera (above).

The giant tusker that bears the Buddha's tooth relic in the perehera, richly garlanded with lights (right).

Each elephant is caparisoned in glittering gold, red, silver or blue cloth, studded with brilliants and lit with lamps. The dignitaries who ride them are scarcely less gorgeously attired. Between the elephants come the drummers, the fire-eaters, musicians and religious and traditional dancers. These are the Nilames or custodians of the relic.

The future of the perehera depends, alas, on the continued existence of enough elephants in the wild to provide tame working animals to take part in this great spectacle.

5

HONG KONG

A ONCE FRAGRANT HARBOUR

THE story goes that many centuries ago some fishermen in the South China Sea were driven north by a typhoon, but were fortunate enough to find themselves in a splendid natural harbour protected by a large island. They sailed round the shoreline of the harbour until they came to a small bay with a large waterfall over which cascaded the purest water. The waterfall was surrounded by sweet-smelling trees that modern botanists say were probably *Aquilaria sinensis*. The fishermen were so enchanted by the scented air that they called the place 'Hong Kong', which means in Chinese 'fragrant harbour'. There are several waterfalls, any of which might be the site of their discovery. The air around each of them is by no means as sweet-smelling as it was then and the water that flows over the falls into the harbour is certainly not as pure.

The British came to Hong Kong in a far different fashion. In 1839, the Chinese decided to end the lucrative opium trade carried on by British merchants. Britain had long coveted Hong Kong as a perfect harbour for its eastern commerce, and the proposed end of the opium trade provided a pretext for war. Britain won the en-

clave, and, in 1860, also acquired on a perpetual lease the Kowloon peninsula, adding in 1898 more islands and the New Territories of mainland China on a 99-year lease. That lease runs out in 1997, when the Chinese are to take back the East's foremost capitalist city, with its six million inhabitants.

China will also take over what is left of the once remarkable flora and fauna. As guardians of its wildlife, Hong Kong's British tenants cannot be said to have done very well, though in the last ten years there have been attempts by Hong Kong conservationists to save what is left. What will happen when China takes over hardly bears thinking about, for that country's record on conservation is not particularly promising.

Since the break-up and dispersal of the supercontinent Pangaea, a process that began at least 200 million years ago, the Kowloon peninsula and Hong Kong and its 242 islands have remained

An aerial view of Kei Wais showing Long Creek in the far background.

112

Old Aberdeen Harbour (above).

Short-tailed macaque (left), once wild in Hong Kong. Now, just across the Chinese border, the rich and fashionable dine off it.

attached to what is now mainland China. Sea levels have risen and fallen with the coming and going of the ice ages as they have everywhere else. At times some of Hong Kong's islands were joined to the mainland; at others some were no doubt submerged. Nevertheless, Hong Kong's flora and fauna are basically that of neighbouring China, though some islands must have been separated long enough to produce their own endemic species.

For the last 6,000 years Hong Kong's coastline has remained unchanged. Hong Kong lies at the southern end of an eroded chain of sedimentary rocks with some granite and volcanic outpourings. Its mountains—the highest, Tai Mo Shan, reaches 3,143 ft (958 m)—were uplifted during the Jurassic period, between 130 and 190 million years ago.

Hong Kong's special interest to the zoologist is that it is situated practically where two zoo-geographical regions meet, the Oriental, in which it actually lies, and the Palaearctic. It is also a key staging post on the route of birds travelling between Siberia and Australasia. From a conservationist viewpoint, Hong Kong's problem can be summed up in a few words: too many people. Moreover, most are not concerned with the environment, with very good reason: they live in extremely crowded conditions with poor amenities, including inadequate sewage and waste disposal. Nor are they conditioned by upbringing or tradition to protect wildlife. In fact, in Hong Kong's markets you can buy almost any creature or part thereof you consider a delicacy, from bear's paw to braised dog.

While Hong Kong has passed laws against the killing of rare species for food, there is little doubt that the trade still goes on, hunters operating in Burma and China to supply undercover markets. Raids on fourteen Hong Kong restaurants in 1987 found giant salamanders, pangolins and even golden eagles kept alive to satisfy the whims of gourmet diners. Just across the Chinese border in the city of Shenzhen there is a notorious restaurant where rich Hong Kong merchants can dine off clouded leopard, eagle owl, macaque, or python—in season or, for that matter, out of it—and sometimes tiger soup. It is doubtful whether the diners actually find these offerings delicious. The older generation tends to believe in such dishes as health cures, aphrodisiacs or a source of physical and mental strength, while the prosperous young order them to impress their friends.

This is the black side of the wildlife situation in Hong Kong. It is hard not to emphasize the negative aspects when you consider what Hong Kong still has to offer and is fast losing.

Including Kowloon and the New Territories, Hong Kong has forty species of mammals, 350 species of birds including residents and migrants, seventy species of reptiles, twenty species of amphibians, 200 butterfly and 2,300 plant species. Some of these, such as the monkeys (including macaques), have been introduced in the past, though they were undoubtedly present in the not-

115

Black kites can still be seen soaring between the sky-scrapers. They nest on Stonecutter's Island, a high security army site. Now even the island's future is uncertain.

so-distant past and before the Chinese ate them all. There are also endemic species—animals and plants that exist nowhere else. These include the Hong Kong newt, Hong Kong cascade frog and the Hong Kong slipper orchid. There are also animals that are listed in the IUCN's Red Data Book of Endangered Species. These include water birds such as Swinhoe's egret and the Asian dowitcher and reptiles such as the Burmese python.

For simplicity's sake, Hong Kong, Kowloon and the New Territories can be divided into three main habitats, all of which are under threat: the sea, including the coastline; the hills with remaining woodland; and the marshland.

An Uncertain Future

Hong Kong's Victoria Harbour is used by over a quarter of a million ships a year. Domestic and industrial waste, discharged oil and millions of gallons of raw sewage are flushed into the sea every day. But there are still fish in the harbour. They would long ago have vanished but for the fact that a powerful tide daily takes most of this pollution out to sea. But the young fish still suffer and stocks are dwindling, so that fish-eating birds such as the reef egret are decreasing in numbers.

In the middle of the shipping lanes there is, for the moment, a sanctuary for nesting birds, including the black kites that scavenge Hong Kong's streets and soar on the updraughts between the towering office blocks. Stonecutter's Island has changed little since the British colonized Hong Kong. The reason why it provides a nesting sanctuary for the kite, Hong Kong's most spectacular bird of prey, is that it is a high-security site for the army. But it may not remain so for long, for there are already plans to develop a recreational complex on the island and to instal a much-needed sewage treatment plant. If this happens, someone will have to rid Stonecutter's Island of its very large and varied snake population. During the Second World War, the Japanese produced anti-snakebite serums there. Before they surrendered, the Japanese army turned all the snakes loose. Their descendants are thriving, a hazard to the nesting birds, including the black kites.

Hong Kong's coastline stretches for 500 miles (800 km). Until the 1940s, its beaches teemed with wildlife. Now these are rapidly being poisoned, some by the sewage that the tide takes away from Victoria Harbour. Tolo Harbour, in the north-eastern part of the New Territories, is one of the most threatened areas. Its mangrove swamps are rapidly being wiped out by pollution from the satellite towns that are springing up along the shore. One beach has so far managed to stay comparatively healthy. At Ting-Kok migrants such as the grey-rumped sandpiper, who have travelled all the way from Siberia, feed on several species of crabs after their long journey. The sand octopus, the smallest octopus in the world, can still be found at Ting-Kok. It is so tiny that it can live inside an empty clam shell whence it emerges to seize minute soldier crabs.

On a remote beach on the western coast, the last survivors of one of Hong Kong's rarest marine creatures still come into the shallows to breed. The giant king crabs choose nights when the tide is highest and the moon full. The females, some of whom are the size of a dustbin lid, lay their eggs in the sand under about 18 in (45 cm) of water. King crab is, in fact, a misnomer. These creatures are not crustaceans at all but prehistoric members of the spider family. It seems that their day, too, is numbered in Hong Kong.

Twenty years ago the city's population never thought of spending a day at the beach. These days many more people have money and more leisure to enjoy it. A new road runs along the west coast, so the beaches are no longer deserted, and litter of all sorts is left behind in great quantities. Several beaches have become so polluted that they are now closed. In any case, the king crabs are unlikely to survive long, for the Chinese eat them and their eggs, believing them to be an aphrodisiac. The outlook for this once beautiful natural coast, its mangroves and marine life looks bleak. And there is little to suggest that it will improve when China takes over.

Shoreline dwellers: a king crab (top left), not a crab at all but a prehistoric member of the spider family; spider crabs (top right) and a crab-hunting reef egret.

In the hills behind this rapidly declining coastline, unspoilt country still exists. Hong Kong sits just below the Tropic of Cancer. In summer the temperature can soar to over 40°C (104°F). Yet the hillsides are surprisingly lush. This is because the hottest time coincides with the typhoon season. Clouds blow in from the Pacific laden with moisture. The warm, damp air is forced up the hillsides and the clouds shed torrents of tropical rain. Streams swell in minutes and waterfalls get a sudden new lease of life. The storms seldom last long and the floods subside almost as quickly as they arise.

Amphibians, crustaceans and fish

Two species of pelican visit Hong Kong on migration. (left). Their future depends on threatened marshlands.

Great and little egrets feed in marshy shallows (below). A new airport may still threaten many bird species.

that live in such conditions have to evolve some method of holding on if they are not to be swept away and end up in the sea. The endemic Hong Kong cascade frog has evolved suction pads on the end of each toe with which it can cling to the slippery rocks when the flash-floods strike. The zebra loach has become so specialized that it cannot survive in a less turbulent environment. Its ventral fins are enlarged and flattened to form suckers on the underside of the body. It creeps over the boulders on the beds of the mountain streams, grazing on algae. Long-armed freshwater shrimps wedge themselves in cracks when the river rises.

The government has, alas, enclosed some of the mountain streams in concrete banks to prevent land erosion. Much of the former forests has been cleared by cutting and burning. Woodland has become grassland, forcing the forest animals on to the retreat. Only a few, such as the highly adaptable wild pigs, have been able to cope with the changed and still changing landscape. One part of the mountain habitat has been changed by man to the benefit of one species of mammal. Many of the hillsides are honeycombed with old mine tunnels. Recently, bent-winged bats were found to have colonized them. Since bats are considered by the Chinese to be symbols of good luck they are one creature that is likely to remain safe when the British hand over Hong Kong.

Perhaps the best hope of all is in the extreme north-west of the New Territories, in the Deep Bay area on the eastern bank of the Pearl River. The Mai Po marshes that abut the present Chinese border are the last marshes

left in Hong Kong. Even more important, they are the only (partly) protected wetlands in Southern China. They are the vital staging post for millions of birds migrating between Siberia and Australasia.

The whole area of mud-flats and mangrove swamps in Deep Bay is vital to the future well-being of this key oriental flyway. The Worldwide Fund for Nature has managed to buy one-sixth of the Mai Po marshes as a

A stately purple heron (above). Hong Kong is a vital staging point between Siberia and Australasia.

A black-crowned night heron is to be found amongst the reeds of Mai Po marshes (right).

nature reserve, but the protected area is nothing like sufficient to cope with all the needs of the bird traffic that pours through the area, especially with its diversified feeding demands.

For the remaining five-sixths of Deep Bay the threats are ever-present. Until recently they included plans to build a second airport. The presence of a population of seldom fewer than 2,000 cormorants, 20,000 gulls (including the rarest of all gulls, Saunders' gull), 15,000 ducks, 5,000 herons and 10,000 waders must have conjured up nightmare pictures of the risk of birdstrikes. A jet engine that sucks in a flock of waders is inevitably a dead jet engine. Whatever the reason, the planners abandoned the idea. It would be pleasant to think that this decision was made purely

on conservation and environmental grounds, but on all the evidence of the past this seems unlikely. Though the threat to build the airport seems to have receded, there is still talk of setting up a dumping ground for toxic waste close to the marshes.

It is easy enough to point out what is wrong with Hong Kong environmentally but far from easy to find solutions. The population pressures on this comparatively small and beautiful place are probably too great for anyone to solve. The present government has done something by designating 40 per cent of the territory as country parkland where plants and animals are supposed to be protected. However, such land is intended to be used by hikers and campers, many of whom show little

respect for rare reptiles, in particular harmless water snakes, and even pangolins and pythons.

As everywhere else in the world, changing these attitudes requires a long campaign of education. To be fair, the government of Hong Kong has such pressing social problems on its hands that it can spare little time either for passing or, equally important, enforcing conservation laws. Anyway, time is running out, as 1997 bears down on Hong Kong. After that, the future is in China's hands.

(Above) The head of Hong Kong's most handsome bird of prey, the black kite. This is a juvenile. A colony of bent-winged bats, often found in the old mine workings (right).

6

LIKE NOTHING ELSE

ON EARTH

EACH zoogeographical region of the world contains creatures that occur nowhere else. In this respect the Oriental Region is rich. It not only has unique species, but unique families and even a unique order. The distribution of these unfamiliar and fascinating animals is closely linked to the effects that geological forces have had on the land in which they live.

To begin with, these forces have created the most formidable barrier to animal movement on earth. Two hundred million years ago, after the great southern super-continent Pangaea started to break up, India began its drift northward on its tectonic plate. It did so at the rate of 4-7 in (10-18 cm) per year until it collided with the Laurasian land mass (North America and Eurasia, which were then joined). The collision is still occurring as the plate on which India sits is 'subducted' beneath the Eurasian land mass. This has resulted in the gradual piling up of the Himalayas.

Some geologists say that this uplift happened as recently, geologically speaking, as 45,000 years ago. The pressure is still on, though experts now believe that the Himalayas have almost reached their maximum height as the result of the collision. Sheer weight of mountain mass may even be melting the base rocks on which the Himalayas stand. That is the latest theory. What is certain is that for countless ages the greatest mountain range on earth will continue to form an impenetrable barrier to the terrestrial animals that live north and south of it. Only migrating birds, such as bar-headed geese, are capable of crossing the peak of Everest.

The rate at which the Indian and Eurasian plates collide has slowed down since the Eocene —some 50 to 30 million years ago—to half its original rate. Even so, 2 in (5 cm) of movement a year is enough to account for practically all the seismic, volcanic and tectonic activity in South-East Asia. This huge area, which includes Thailand, Burma, Laos, Cambodia, Malaysia and Indonesia, is sometimes referred to as Indosinia.

India has made perhaps the most dramatic move of all the shifting land masses. By contrast,

The sun sets on Everest. The Himalayas have proved an impassable barrier to terrestrial animals.

126

The vegetation of the Kingdoms of the East is as varied as the animals that live in them. In a short distance you can travel from lush tropical forest to frozen pools and ice-water scree.

Indosinia has remained anchored to the south-east corner of Laurasia since the start of geological history. Though it has remained in much the same place, it has undergone very extensive modifications and these have profoundly influenced the distribution of its wildlife. Plate movements may not have altered South-East Asia's global position, yet they have pushed up mountains and even caused Indosinia to tilt. This happened in the late Tertiary between three and twelve million years ago. The tilt drowned the eastern and southern parts, forming the South China Sea and the Gulf of Thailand. At that time mammals were at the height of their evolutionary diversification. However, the tilting process and inundation that accompanied it were so gradual that most existing forms of wildlife had ample time to escape from or adapt to the changes.

The inundations that came later with the four major ice ages between three million and 10,000

One of the East's unique species, the colugo, a gliding mammal, here with a baby clutched to its breast (above). Dhallagiri in Nepal, the peak that looks like a fish tail (right).

years ago played a dramatic part in the distribution of animals and in the evolution and survival of some of the unique species and subspecies of the Oriental Region.

In the mid-Pleistocene, between one and two million years ago, the sea level around South-East Asia was as much as 660 ft (200 m) lower than it is today. Borneo, Java and Sumatra were all connected to the mainland by what is known as the Sunda Shelf, just as Australia and New Guinea were joined by the Sahul Shelf. Between the two shelves lay Celebes (now Sulawesi), the Lesser Sunda islands, the Moluccas and the Philippines.

130

The dense, lush forests harbour many little known and rarely seen creatures, like this diminutive mouse deer (above). Tropical forests undergo little seasonal change so they provide a constant suppply of food for creatures such as this fruit bat, also known as a flying fox (right).

The advance and retreat of the last glaciation caused sea-level changes to take place there very recently, in geological terms. A mere 18,000 years ago, the sea was 280 ft (85 m) lower than it is now. Yet 8,000 years ago the sea stood 25-50 ft (8-15 m) higher than it is today.

These changing levels allowed many offshore islands to become populated with mainland forms, many of which evolved, as a result of long isolation, into separate subspecies and even distinct species. One small island, Koh Terutau, off Thailand, has at least nine endemic subspecies of squirrels, five of common tree shrews and three of lesser mouse deer. The Mentawi group of four islands, the largest of which is Siberut, lie only 53-84 miles (85-135 km) off the west coast of Sumatra. Yet they have a genus of langur monkey known nowhere else in the Oriental Region. Sixty-five per cent of their mammals are endemic, including all four of their primate species. The reason is that the Mentawi islands have been isolated from Sumatra for between 50,000 and one million years.

As everywhere else on earth, climate has played a large part in the distribution of species, as have vegetational changes, which are the direct result of climatic variation. During the warmer, wetter periods such as the Miocene, between 15 and 25 million years ago, many species now found in the tropics—gibbons and orang-utans, for example—ranged much further north. Over the ages the traffic has flowed south from mainland China and Burma into Sumatra, Java and Borneo as well as north again as rising and falling sea levels and climate dictated.

These varying conditions, all taking place over a comparatively short time, have had spectacular effects on the evolution of the mammals of South-East Asia. Falling sea levels periodically gave mainland species, isolated on islands for thousands of years, the opportunity to join up again. By then some of them had diverged far enough from their original forms to become new species, and were no longer genetically capable of breeding with their mainland ancestors. Many of these new species survived, notably squirrels, rats and bats. Thus the forests of the Malay peninsula, Thailand and Burma and Indo-China acquired a rich and diverse mammalian fauna. Climate and geology had combined in this part of the Oriental Region to produce ideal conditions for the creation of new species and subspecies.

The one order, several families and many species that are now unique to the Oriental Region make up a strange and fascinating collection of little-known animals.

Nearly all these wildlife 'one-offs' are inhabitants of the tropical forests. Most are tree-dwellers and range in size from minute to small. Living side by side with them in those forests are a great many extremely interesting creatures that are *not* unique to the Oriental Region but have much the same lifestyle and some of the same physical characteristics. To avoid confusion, the first mention below of each of the exclusively oriental animals appears in italics.

The tropical forests can provide a home for such a specialized and diverse fauna because they undergo very little seasonal change. This means that there are plenty of fruit, seeds, and leaves in the upper canopy all year round. The first characteristic of any mammal that seeks to make the

A small group of islands off Thailand even has a genus of langur monkeys unknown anywhere else in the Oriental Region. The grey langurs seen here (left) are perched in a bombax, or kapok, tree. The colugo (above) is an efficient glider as well as climber.

most of this abundant harvest is sufficient lightness to climb and move about among the slenderest and highest branches. It helps if it is small, and it is also a great advantage if it can easily reach the next tree without having to climb down to the ground and then climb up again. Bats have no problem here. There are many forest species, including flying foxes, or fruit bats, some of which have a wing-span of 5 ft (1.5 m). They are, however, the only flying mammals. The next best thing to flying is gliding. The tropical forests of the Far East have more gliding mammals than anywhere else, including Australia.

If only because they are the sole member of their order, the Dermoptera, which means 'skin-winged', the *colugos* must take pride of place. They are often called 'flying lemurs', but this is a complete misnomer, for lemurs occur only in Madagascar. There are two species of colugo, the Malayan and the Philippine.

Colugos are active mainly at night. When at rest during the daytime, the animal looks as though it is wrapped in a camouflaged fur blanket that matches the bark of the branch to which it clings, head uppermost. This 'blanket' is a generous fold of skin stretching from the side of the neck to the tips of fingers and toes and extending to the tip of the long tail on each side of the body. From nose to tail the whole animal is about 16 in (40 cm) long.

When moving about the forest canopy at night in search of food, the colugo opens its 'parachute', and makes long, controlled glides between individual trees and across forest clearings. Mothers even carry their young clutched to them when airborne. A 'flight' of 446 ft (136 m) has been recorded, during which the animal lost only 30-40 ft (10-12 m) in height, a glide ratio of better than one in ten. Colugos have no problems in making up the height lost when gliding. They are equipped with sharp nails and are excellent climbers.

Zoologists have had great difficulty in classifying colugos. At various times they have regarded them as insectivores, although they do not eat insects; as bats, although their gliding membranes bear no resemblance to the wings of a bat; as primates, because of the construction of their middle ear. Experts now solve the problem by placing them in a separate order which, they believe, branched off a very long time ago and did not lead to more advanced forms. Colugos differ in so many ways from other mammals that they thoroughly merit an order of their own. Even their teeth are differently arranged and their front teeth are divided like combs, either for straining juice from fruit or for grooming.

Many other animals of the tropical forests have adapted themselves to some means of gliding. There are many species of 'flying' squirrels, but none of these is so well equipped for flight as the colugo, their gliding membranes being not nearly so extensive. Perhaps most extraordinary are the flying reptiles and amphibians of Asia. The paradise tree snakes of Sumatra, Java and Borneo, and the golden tree snakes of India, Burma, Thailand and Indo-China can contract their undersides into a concave shape that acts like a

parachute. When they launch themselves into the air they suddenly straighten their bodies and hollow out their lower surfaces.

Eight-inch (20 cm) flying lizards that live in the forests of Sumatra, Java and Borneo can make glides of up to 66 ft (20 m) on membranes supported by elongated ribs that spread out from the body in flight. Geckos have similar membranes but increase their gliding surfaces by means of webbed feet and flaps surrounding the entire body. Gliding frogs use much the same devices but can also, like the snakes, make the underside of their bodies concave. Lizards and geckos are equipped with sharp claws and gripping toe pads to help them cling on after making a crash landing on a tree.

One of the few animals to defeat the Himalayas – the bar-headed goose (left) is thought to cross the peak of Everest on migration. Traditionally terraced fields in Nepal cannot always prevent water running off fields and causing floods (below).

EARLY MAMMALS

The oriental forests also contain small creatures that perhaps give us a glimpse of the kind of animals that, 70 million years ago, led to the evolution of the first placental mammals and so to humans. It is thought that the very first placental mammals were tiny insectivores, but no fossil evidence of them remains. It is very probable, however, that they resembled a family of small forest animals unique to the Oriental Region and known to science as the Tupaiidae. Their common name is *tree shrew*. There are five genera and seventeen species. Their family name comes from the Malay *tupai*, meaning small, squirrel-like animal. The term's local usage covers not only squirrels and tree shrews but also some forest rats. Tree shrews are, however, easily distinguished from squirrels by their long, pointed noses.

The taxonomists have had some difficulty in placing tree shrews in the right zoological category. Until recently they were thought to be primitive primates but now science has put them firmly among the insectivores. One expert has described them as 'the most primate-like non-primate'.

Tree shrews are usually 6-10 in (15-25 cm) in length with a tail as long again as their body. They have five fully formed digits on each hand and foot. The first finger and thumb are capable of quite a lot of flexibility, which enables them to grasp like primates. The ears are small and thick and similar in shape to those of primate species. However, these resemblances are probably 'convergences', similarities acquired as the result of similar needs rather than evidence of a direct connection with true primates.

Tree shrews are found from Borneo to India, where the Madras tree shrew extends its range from the forest into scrub land. They are nervous, often aggressive little creatures and the habits of separate species differ greatly. Some are solitary; others, such as the mountain tree shrew of Borneo, are sociable and live in groups. Common tree shrews live singly or in pairs. Most keep to the trees but the terrestrial and Philippine species live on the ground and nest in holes.

Despite being classified as insectivores, tree shrews are catholic in their tastes. They eat any small creature they can find and subdue, as well as fruits. Most are diurnal foragers, but the feather-tailed species found in parts of Indo-China, Sumatra, Java and Borneo is nocturnal. Tree shrews are a prime example of speciation, whereby a family branches out to create separate species that can take advantage of the many food niches in the rich tropical habitat.

The females build nests, give birth to their blind and hairless young after a gestation of thirty days. They feed their babies only once every 48 hours but cram them so full of milk that, after feeding, it accounts for three-fifths of the infant's body weight.

The very first mammals were small insectivores, probably very similar to this modern tree shrew.

The many small creatures of the oriental forests support a population of small predators. Some, such as the civets, are represented in other zoogeographical regions. The largest of the civets, the binturong, hardly qualifies as a small predator, since it can grow to 3 ft (90 cm) in length. Other members of the civet family (the Viveridae) are the spotted and banded linsang and the rasse. The male of the latter is a solitary night hunter of the forest floor that only meets another rasse to mate and leaves rearing the young to the female.

There is one small predatory species that is exclusive to the region, the *Malayan moon rat*, or *gymnure*. Excluding its tail which is long, bare and rat-like, it measures 8–10 in (20–25 cm) and weighs 2–3 lb (0.9–1.4 kg). The moon rat is an extremely odd-looking animal. It is related to the hedgehog, or rather it belongs to the same family of insectivores. The head and snout alone bear some superficial likeness to those of that familiar creature. The moon rat, which is not a rat at all, is a genuine 'one-off'.

Moon rats live in swampy land, forest and cultivated areas, and in the latter have been known to gnaw the bark off young rubber trees. But they prefer wet places where they can hunt for frogs, fish, molluscs, crustaceans and worms. They are found through most of South-East Asia, including Borneo.

Moon rats have an irritable nature and can hardly be described as attractive. They have a very strong smell that has been likened to a variety of disagreeable substances, from stale sweat to rotten onions. This emanates from two anal glands when the owner becomes excited.

The region does have two primate species that are exclusively its own. The gibbon family, the Hylobatidae is one of these. Gibbons belong to the higher primates, the Anthropoidea, the monkeys and apes. The lower primates are known as the Prosimii, or prosimians. This suborder, which is further down the evolutionary scale, includes the Tarsiidae, or *tarsiers*.

The orient has three species of tarsiers. They all owe their existence to the fact that they live on

Moon rats, or gymnures, occur only in the oriental region. They are very distantly related to hedgehogs.

islands such as Borneo, Sulawesi and the Philippines, where they have had to face less competition. Despite the fact that they are at the most 6 in (15 cm) long, they can make leaps of up to 6 ft (1.8 m). The tips of the fingers and toes are equipped with sucker-like discs that help them to cling on, and the long tail is used as a balance and brake when leaping from branch to branch. The huge eyes, placed in true primate fashion on the front of the face, are those of a nocturnal hunter and feeder. When fast asleep during the day, the tarsier clings, hunched up, by means of its sucker discs to a vertical tree shoot. Extra support is given by the scaly underside of the tail, which is pressed hard against the stem to which the animal is clinging. Tarsiers feed mainly on insects and their larvae but can catch small lizards, fledgling birds, spiders and forest mice. They catch their prey and tear it apart with their hands.

There are three other, far larger animals that are unique to the Oriental Region. All are found in India. The ancestors of practically all the animals that live on the vast plains of western India originally came from the deserts of North Africa and the Middle East. Among the antelope these include gazelle species that have adapted to life in India. There are two antelope, however, that are

The binturong, largest of the civet family, grows to 3 ft (91 cm) in length. A young binturong (upper right) will grow to be a predator of the forest floor.

uniquely Indian. Both the *nilgai* and the *four-horned antelope* were originally Indian woodland species that have adapted to life on the plains. The nilgai is a very large horse-like antelope whose range includes Tibet. The name comes from the Hindustani word *nil* meaning blue and the Persian word for cow, *gau*. The antelope's coat certainly has a bluish tinge, though there is nothing particularly cow-like in its rather beautiful appearance.

The nilgai's woodland ancestry shows in the fact that it inhabits areas where there are at least some trees to give shelter during the hottest part of the day. They do not need to drink a lot, though, getting most of their water from the vegetation they eat. The males, often referred to as 'blue bulls', command breeding territories of around 200 acres (80 hectares), which they mark out with dung piles. During the breeding season in November and December, the dominant bulls gather a harem of anything from two to ten cows. To impress and drive away lesser males, the harem bull develops a darker coat and a swollen neck.

The other, the four-horned antelope, is far stranger in appearance. It is the only mammal, let

141

alone the only antelope, with two pairs of horns. The larger pair are sited normally—well back on top of the skull. The front pair point slightly forward from the forehead and are positioned more or less between the eyes. Both nilgai and four-horned antelope now exist only in greatly reduced and fragmented populations.

The last of the unique species is an Indian reptile, in its way as unusual in appearance as the four-horned antelope. The *gharial* or *gavial* is the only member of its family. The crocodilians are surely one of the most successful groups of animals on earth. They have been around, practically unchanged, for at least 200 million years. Today there are two families, the Crocodylidae and the Gavialidae. Members of the first family, which includes crocodiles, alligators and caymans, all have very much the same appearance, though naturally there are differences, in dentition for

This black and white Oriental tree snake is also known as a flying snake and can 'fly' considerable distances.

example. Nevertheless, an ordinary person might be hard put to tell one from the other. There is no such difficulty in identifying the gharial.

The gharial has evolved the most extraordinarily long, slim, almost beak-like jaws, which have been described as looking like the handle of a saucepan. There are up to twenty-nine teeth in the upper jaw and twenty-five or twenty-six in the lower. The teeth are longer and more slender than in any other crocodilian. Their purpose is to hold fish, which the reptile catches with sideways sweeps of its jaws. The gharial is a poor walker on land but it is probably the most aquatic crocodilian of all. For a reptile that lives almost entirely on fish, it is a very large animal indeed. The shape of the jaws makes it difficult to swallow mammals and there are no records of man-eating. Unconfirmed reports speak of a specimen reaching 30 ft (9 m) in length but the longest authenticated measurement is 21 ft (6.5 m).

The American naturalist William T. Hornaday gives this excellent description of the reptile: 'Gharials are the smoothest of all the large crocodiles I have been privileged to handle. They are also the brightest in colour. Lying upon the sand at a distance of 200 yards [180 m], their bodies often seem to be a uniform dull chrome yellow, but in reality the entire upper surface of the animal from snout to tail is of a uniform olive green, mottled with the former colour. Of course, older individuals lose the original brightness of their colouring with advancing age. The under surfaces are all pale yellow, the eye frosted with black while the pupil is a very narrow, perpendicular black line.'

Adult males sometimes have a strange excrescence on the tip of their snouts. Various theories have been put forward to explain this. One is that it is a hollow that can hold extra air, allowing the reptile to remain submerged longer. But why only males should be given this extra piece of breathing apparatus has not satisfactorily been explained. Its real purpose may be to convey male status in display. Gharial females bury up to forty eggs, usually in two tiers separated from each other by a thick layer of sand. The gharial needs all the breeding help it can get, for it now rates as an endangered species. Artificial breeding programmes are being conducted in India and in Nepal.

Perhaps the strangest fact about this very strange reptile is its circumscribed distribution. It exists only in the river systems of the Ganges and the Brahmaputra. Presumably it evolved in these rivers and their tributaries. It has never been able to reach the Godavari, Tapti or Nerbudda systems, even though their northern tributaries are very close to the source streams of the Ganges. When it comes to mysteries about the distribution of creatures of the Oriental Region, the local nature of that of the gharial is possibly the greatest of them all.

A gharial crocodile; it has a particularly prominent tip to its nose and catches fish with a sideways sweep of its slender jaws.

7

ORANG-UTAN

MAN OF THE FOREST

BETWEEN 38 and 54 million years ago, during the age known as the Eocene, the earth experienced a great expansion of mammalian species. Among these were several families of primates. The three most successful were the Adapidae, the Tarsiidae and the Omomyidae.

The first probably had long snouts and are thought to have been the ancestors of the lemurs, now only found in Madagascar, and of the lorises that today live in the forests of the Far East. The Tarsiidae had shorter noses and primitive teeth. The modern tarsiers live in the same kind of habitat as the lorises.

The most important family—at least from man's point of view since he is descended from it —were the Omomyidae.

Fossils show that until the end of the Eocene period a land bridge connected Eurasia with North America. The early primates crossed this. In North America they died out, perhaps because of unsuitable climate or habitat or both. Those who had carried on far enough reached South America, which much later became cut off when the seas rose across the isthmus of Panama. Before the land bridge to North America emerged above the waters once again they had been isolated long enough to evolve as New World monkeys whose modern descendants walk on all fours and many of whom have prehensile tails. They are thought to have evolved these tails, lacking in all Old World monkeys, because they needed an extra 'hand' to cope with life in forests that were often flooded.

In the Old World, the Omomyidae were highly successful, crowding out the two other families, who were only able to make a living by becoming nocturnal. One of the Omomyidae's greatest successes was that they gave rise to a higher family of primates, the Anthropoidea, which now include monkeys, apes and man.

These advanced primates had large brains and eyes at the front of the face that gave them stereoscopic forward vision. Perhaps most important, they had an opposable thumb. This was separated from the other digits, giving their

The orang-utan is the primate most closely related to man; its lively facial expressions show remarkable similarities to those of humans.

146

About 50 million years ago, the Tarsiidae were one of three successful primate families. The modern tarsier's primate features include stereoscopic vision and gripping fingers.

owners the ability to grasp and manipulate objects. Their finger tips were sensitive and had flattened nails instead of claws. These primates came down from the trees and gradually learned to walk upright. Their brains became larger. Such abilities and equipment gave them the opportunity to make the big evolutionary breakthrough which eventually lead to *Homo sapiens*.

Palaeontologists believe—although there are different schools of thought about lines of descent —that a creature they have named Proconsul was the ancestor of all modern apes. It was also probably a link that led through several species of hominids, some of which died out, to man. Proconsul lived in Africa 15–25 million years ago. Living largely on the ground, it no longer needed a tail. Science places Proconsul in the family Pongidae, to which belong the three species of today's great apes. Scientists are divided about which of the great apes evolved first from the Proconsul line. Most think that the orang-utan branched off before the gorilla and the chimpanzee. Others regard the orang simply as a large relative of the gibbons, who, it is often forgotten, are also apes. All are agreed that the orang-utan is the great ape most distantly connected with man. Superficially at least *Homo sapiens* more closely resembles both the chimpanzee and the gorilla.

Today orang-utans exist only in two islands of the Far East, Borneo and Sumatra. Sumatra belongs to Indonesia. Borneo is divided between Indonesia and Malaysia. Orangs occur in two areas of the Indonesian part of the island and in Sarawak and Sabah, which belong to Malaysia.

They were once far more widely distributed. Fossilized orang-utan teeth—most of what zoologists know of ape evolution comes from the study of fossil teeth—reveal that half a million years ago the orang's ancestors were far bigger and probably twice as heavy as the modern animal. The big male orangs of today's tropical forests find travel in the treetops difficult enough. The far bigger prehistoric apes must have found it much harder and therefore have been much more terrestrial. John Mackinnon, who did much of the pioneer fieldwork on orangs and gives an entertaining account of his studies in *In Search of the Red Ape*, theorizes that the early orangs ranged the ground in large bands like gorillas, protected by their giant males.

Fossil evidence reveals that these giants occupied the woodlands and mountain forests of southern China until the ice ages drove them south into what are now the islands of Sumatra and Borneo. This happened at a time when the ice had, so to speak, sucked up much of the sea. There were then land bridges joining Malaya to Sumatra and Java as well as China to Borneo, the Philippines and Formosa.

149

big evolutionary adjustment. Originally, the giant orangs had evolved in semi-tropical forests to the north where much of their food could be found at ground level. They were now restricted to tropical rain forests where most of their food plants grew in the upper canopy. Provided the trees would support an orang's weight, the canopy not only provided food but a convenient means of forest travel and freedom from ground predators. Two things happened. Treetop living favoured the lighter animals. Natural selection saw to it that these were the ones to survive so that in time the orang became substantially smaller. Second, in the forest canopy it was no longer an advantage to live in large groups. A large family party would quickly devour all the food in one area. Nor was the protection of a big male (as with gorilla families) needed. So the species became smaller and the former large groups dispersed. The orang-utan became the more or less solitary animal it is today.

Change in habitat was not the only pressure the orang-utan faced in the three islands in which it now lived. During the Pleistocene, Stone Age man appeared on the scene in Java and spread quickly. The fertile lowlands are always the first places to be occupied and Java was no exception. The orangs were gradually forced back into the mountain forests. Early man found the apes easy to kill, even with primitive weapons. Bones found in caves show that orangs were regularly hunted for the pot. In Java, it was not long before the species was wiped out. What saved the orang, at least temporarily, in Sumatra and Borneo was that the mountainous terrain was far less appealing to early man. Even modern man made comparatively little impact on the orang-utan's habitat there until after the Second World War. Since then the picture has changed incredibly fast so that now it seems possible that the extinction that took place in Java may be repeated.

Orang-utan means, in Malay, 'man of the forest'. The orang is also often referred to as 'the red ape' after the colour of its covering of shaggy hair. It seems likely that originally the coastal tribes applied the name orang-utan to the wild tribes of the interior. It is also probable that the

Today orang-utans survive only in Borneo and Sumatra.

(Right) Another primitive primate, the slow loris, occupies much the same habitat as the tarsier.

When the ice melted and the seas rose again, the climate to the north became friendly to orangs once more. But by now the rising waters had isolated them on the islands of Borneo, Sumatra and Java.

These marooned populations had to make a

The name orang-utan comes from the Malay and means 'man of the forest' (left).

(Above) A female siamang holding young. Siamangs and the closely allied gibbons are apes too, not very distant from the orang itself.

153

many forest tribes who were familiar with orang-utans simply regarded them as a different-looking lot of wild people. Whatever the origin of the name, it is a very appropriate one. The orang is by far the most arboreal of the great apes. The man of the forest cannot survive long if his forest home disappears.

The outside world first became aware of the word 'orang-utan' in 1641, when a Dutchman called Nicholas Tulp used it to refer to an ape brought to Europe. Zoological accuracy was not Tulp's strong point. The animal was a chimpanzee shipped from Africa. In the 1750s, orangs from Sumatra reached Holland, but it was not until the 1850s that the English scientist Alfred Wallace (see page 164) actually saw orangs in the wild and inevitably collected specimens by shooting them, the way that even the best naturalists obtained animals for study in those days.

There is only one species of orang-utan and two races. The Sumatran race is slightly taller and slimmer and has a narrower face than its Bornean neighbour. The main difference is in colour. As a rule an orang from Borneo is darker, though orangs differ in appearance almost as much as people.

Perhaps the orang's most outstanding feature is the length of its arms. Unlike their relatives the gibbons, orangs do not leap, though they can swing from tree to tree, a process known as brachiation. They move mainly by climbing, gripping with their flexible toes and progressing with the ease with which we walk on level ground. Occasionally they walk upright along a branch, grasping it with their toes but always holding on to a branch above their heads with their hands. When they descend to the forest floor they walk awkwardly on all fours, treading on the sides of their clenched feet and placing their hands on the ground.

Adult males are very intimidating animals. They stand 4½ ft (1.4 m) tall and weigh up to 220 lb (100 kg). (The females weigh around half as much and are about 8 in (20 cm) shorter.) The face of the adult male develops inflatable muscular cheek flaps. Below the chin is a pouch that hangs

Young Sumatran orang sampling a leaf. At the Bohorok rehabilitation centre, orangs due for release in the forest must first learn which wild foods are good to eat.

down like a dewlap. Some of these patriarchs grow magnificent beards and moustaches, the whole effect giving them the appearance of an Old Testament prophet. This terrifying face has evolved to impress.

The big males tend to be solitary. They are also extremely vocal, calling and bellowing a good deal of the time. The usual motive behind such an outstanding display of male power is to attract females. With the orang this does not appear to be the case; rather the reverse in fact. So what is it all about? John Mackinnon's theory is interesting. The success of an individual in biological terms depends on his ability to leave successful descendants. But success cannot be measured merely in numbers of offspring. The offspring have to be able to reproduce in their turn and this means that they must have sufficient food and space in which to breed.

Mackinnon suggests that by advertising his own aggression and bad temper the patriarch may be spoiling his own chances of further reproductive activity but his display also ruins the chances

Orangs are the most arboreal of the apes. When on the ground, they walk on the sides of their clenched feet and support themselves with their hands.

of his male neighbours. He therefore ensures that the orang population within his home range is kept below its carrying capacity. This guarantees that his own offspring have sufficient space and food in which to grow.

The adult male's reproductive life has two phases. As a sub-adult he fathers offspring. As an adult he protects their future interests. As he grows older he becomes more grotesque and therefore more frightening and effective in his second role.

There is no special mating season. Gestation is slightly shorter than it is for human mothers. The baby weighs only about 3½ lb (1.6 kg) at birth. For the first year it is in continual body contact with its mother, clinging tightly to her as she travels and climbing all over her when she stops. Often an earlier youngster accompanies the pair and may even play with its sibling. But in the main the infant depends on its mother for everything, including play. For at least seven months she breast-feeds her baby. However, it comes to know, and may even sample, favoured food plants that the mother eats.

After some months, the baby learns to walk along branches by holding onto the hairs of its mother's rump. By the second year the young orang is becoming more independent, though it still keeps close to its mother. It can now find some of the seeds, shoots and vines which it has learned by example are good to eat. It still sleeps with its mother in the rudimentary nest she builds for the night but practises building nests for itself. By the third year, the young orang is much more venturesome and will leave its mother for short spells, especially if it meets other youngsters who are willing to play.

The young remain with their mother until a new baby is born, after which they wander further and further away until the parental bond breaks down completely. Young males leave home earlier than females. The latter often stay to play with the new infant, for this is probably the only way they can learn baby care. By the time they produce their own young they are solitaries with no older females around to teach them by example.

Females are ready to breed at about seven years old. From then on they are continually involved in motherhood, producing babies at two to three-year intervals.

Young males are busy right through adolescence establishing their own home ranges and learning the pecking order among the orangs in their part of the forest. Males go on growing well into their teens, when they start developing the facial adornments of the adult, but they are sexually mature at about ten. Courtship is not all smooth going for the young male. For a start he has to find a receptive female—not always easy with animals as solitary and spread about the forest as orangs. Then he has to cope with the alarming vocal displays of the old males, designed to put him off his game. And the females often require considerable persuasion before they will accept their suitor. The steady rate of pregnancy among wild females, however, attests to the efficiency of the system.

These days, sadly, the natural system is not enough to ensure the survival of the species. The unnatural has taken over in the shape of the chain-saw and the bulldozer. The rain forests of Borneo and Sumatra are as much at risk as those of the Amazon basin and they occupy a far smaller area. In this situation anything that can be done to halt the destruction of the forests and to maintain the population of orang-utans in the wild must be attempted. No one can be sure how many are left, but it is probably far fewer than 10,000. The Government of Indonesia and in particular its wildlife organization PPA are doing their best, aided by money from the Worldwide Fund for Nature and the Frankfurt Zoological Society. Orang-utan reserves have been established, such as the Gunung Leuser in Sumatra, as well as four more in Sarawak, Sabah and Borneo. Outside and even around these reserves there is no guarantee of protection for the equally important adjoining forest.

The author's experience is limited to the Gunung Leuser Reserve in Sumatra where he worked on a 'Survival' wildlife film about the orang-utan rehabilitation centre at Bohorok.

There is a similar rehabilitation centre in the north of Gunung Leuser at Ketambe and several more in Borneo. The objectives of these centres are to increase the numbers of orangs living wild and to educate Indonesians and Malaysians in the need to protect both the forests and their inhabitants. The word 'rehabilitation' gives a clue as to how these aims are being achieved.

There has, unfortunately, always been a trade in baby orangs as pets. In Indonesia they are much more: they are regarded as a status symbol. This means they are often in the hands of high officials or the extremely rich—the very people who are hardest to persuade to give up their illegal captives. Sadly, the easiest way to capture a baby orang is almost invariably to kill the mother. This is far more damaging to the wild population than simply kidnapping an infant. Their owners find the young orangs charming pets until they begin to grow up. Orangs are sometimes called 'the mechanical ape'. They have a talent for using as a lever planks or anything else that comes to hand. Only a very strong cage will then hold them. There is plenty of evidence, too, that orangs kept in cramped solitary confinement become not only bored but mentally sick.

For over forty years it was illegal in Indonesia to kill, capture or keep an orang-utan in captivity. No one took note of this law until some fifteen years ago when the Indonesian government became an active supporter of orang conservation. Nevertheless, for the scientists running the rehabilitation centres it is still a question of persuading the owners to surrender their captives rather than ordering them to do so. In this they increasingly have the support of the wardens of PPA.

In 1977, when Survival filmed the rehabilitation of orangs in Sumatra, two young Swiss scientists, Regina Frey and Monica Borner, were running the station at Bohorok. In three years they had rounded up fifty captive orangs. Sometimes it took weeks to persuade an owner to surrender his pet. They made it a rule never to pay, never to bribe, never to threaten to prosecute except in the case of dealers who could sell a young orang for

several hundred pounds on the black market.

When a newly freed prisoner arrived at Bohorok it underwent a six-week quarantine. Apes and people can exchange illnesses and diseases, including tuberculosis, pneumonia and polio; the author even caught an unidentified virus from an orang-utan during his time at Bohorok. A quarantine period was essential. Without it, human diseases picked up by contact with their late owners could easily have been spread not only to the other apes at the station but to forest-living orangs with whom they mixed.

The very young inmates at Bohorok had to be taught a surprising number of basic skills, such as how to climb and walk upright on a branch, things they would normally have learned from their mothers.

For their own safety the babies were kept in cages but were handled every day by Regina and Monica. After the quarantine was over and a course of protective injections had been given, the older orangs were gradually introduced to the forest and then allowed to live freely all day. In late afternoon an orang-utans' tea party was held on top of a hill 400 ft (120 m) above the station. About half an hour before this was due to start you

An orang, ready for release in the forest, is carried 15 miles (24 km) away from the Bohorok centre so that it will not be tempted to return for a daily free meal.

could meet up to twenty orangs swinging through the trees where they had spent the day in order to get their free meal. This always included milk and green bananas, though the latter do not feature prominently on a wild orang's menu. The idea was to give them food that was nourishing but not particularly appetizing. They would then have an incentive to seek out wild foods when foraging for themselves during the day. Sometimes, a wild orang would appear out of the forest and gatecrash the party. This was usually discouraged in case the wild ape became too dependent on hand-outs.

The meal would last an hour. It was exactly like a children's tea party, complete with squab-

Orangs are sometimes known as the 'Red Apes'. The young make charming pets, a fact that often leads to their illegal capture. (Right) Tea party at Bohorok feeding station. Young orangs living free in the forest all day return in the afternoon for their meal of bananas and milk. Regina Frey (top) comforts a temperamental orang while an Indonesian wildlife ranger tries to stop others quarrelling over the milk.

bling and displays of temperament. One soon discovered that orangs, like people, have different personalities and are childlike in their sudden show of frustration, anger and even affection.

Orangs are curious by nature. This one (above) not only switched on the movie camera but ate the rubber eyepiece!

(Left) This time it is only small, soft wood trees that have been felled. Too often axe and chainsaw destroy primary rain forest.

When the party was over, all but the very young, who had to be confined to their cages for the night, would find their way back into the forest.

The tea party enabled Regina and Monica to meet their charges each day and monitor their progress. The ultimate aim was to return their orangs to the wild. Before they were judged ready for final release, they had to meet several basic requirements. First they had to be able to travel in the treetops. Then they had to be able to build a nest for the night. Their daily condition showed clearly whether they were capable of finding enough natural food for themselves.

When a batch of orangs was ready for return to the forest they were put in crates and carried by porters up the banks and along the bed of the Bohorok river—the forest there is far too dense to walk through—and released at least 15 miles (24 km) from the station. Had they been set free any nearer they would almost certainly have found their way back for a free meal of milk and green bananas at the orang-utans' tea party.

In three years the two women retrained and released fewer than thirty orangs. Many more have been rehabilitated since. It does not seem a great return for all the time and money expended. But with the world population of this fascinating and endearing ape close to extinction, any effort to stabilize the situation must be worthwhile. The value of the rehabilitation centres extends far beyond the actual numbers released. The attention these centres have attracted has made the illegal trade in baby orangs hard, if not impossible.

The basic problems, however, remain much the same. In recent years the forests on the other side of the river from the Gunung Leuser reserve have been clear-felled. Though these forests are equally important to the orang-utans, they are not part of the reserve. The trees that once sheltered the man of the forest have been chopped down and sold to shelter the man of the city in Tokyo and Nagasaki.

8

WHICH SIDE OF THE LINE?

WHEN the zoologists of the mid-nineteenth century divided the world and its flora and fauna into six zoogeographical regions (see Introduction), the boundaries of most of these zones were self-evident. The Ethiopian Region, for example, which included Africa south of the Sahara as well as Arabia, was almost entirely enclosed by oceans. The Oriental Region was by no means as easy to define. Between it and the Australian Region lay a pattern of great and small islands including Sumatra, Java, Borneo, Bali, Lombok, Celebes, the Sundas, the Moluccas, the Philippines and New Guinea.

Where was the line demarcating the end of the Oriental Region and the start of the Australian Region to be drawn?

The system of zoogeographical regions, now accepted by zoologists throughout the world, was the work of two great Victorian naturalists, Dr P. L. Sclater, who put forward his theories in 1858, and Alfred Russel Wallace, who set down his conclusions in a classic book eighteen years later. In *The Malay Archipelago*, Wallace describes eight years of study and collecting specimens among the islands of South-East Asia and the conclusions he reached about the distribution of their wildlife. The Victorian era was a time of zoological awakening, unquestionably dominated by Charles Darwin. The religious and zoological controversy stirred up by his theories on evolution largely overshadowed the very similar, or at least parallel, work that Wallace had done in the Far East. It is said that Wallace's writings after his return to England persuaded Darwin to publish *The Origin of Species*. The two great men clearly had immense respect for each other. Wallace dedicates his *Malay Archipelago* with these words:

TO

CHARLES DARWIN
AUTHOR OF 'THE ORIGIN OF SPECIES'

I DEDICATE THIS BOOK

*NOT ONLY
AS A TOKEN OF PERSONAL ESTEEM
AND FRIENDSHIP*

*BUT ALSO
TO EXPRESS MY DEEP ADMIRATION
FOR HIS GENIUS AND HIS WORKS*

What Alfred Russel Wallace achieved among the islands of the Malay Archipelago was to delineate the boundary between the Oriental and the Australian regions. He did this so effectively that it is to this day referred to as the Wallace Line. The zoogeographical area that surrounds this line is sometimes called the Wallacean sub-region. Broadly speaking, Wallace put Sumatra, Java, Bali, Borneo and the Philippines in the Oriental Region; New Guinea, Timor and the smaller

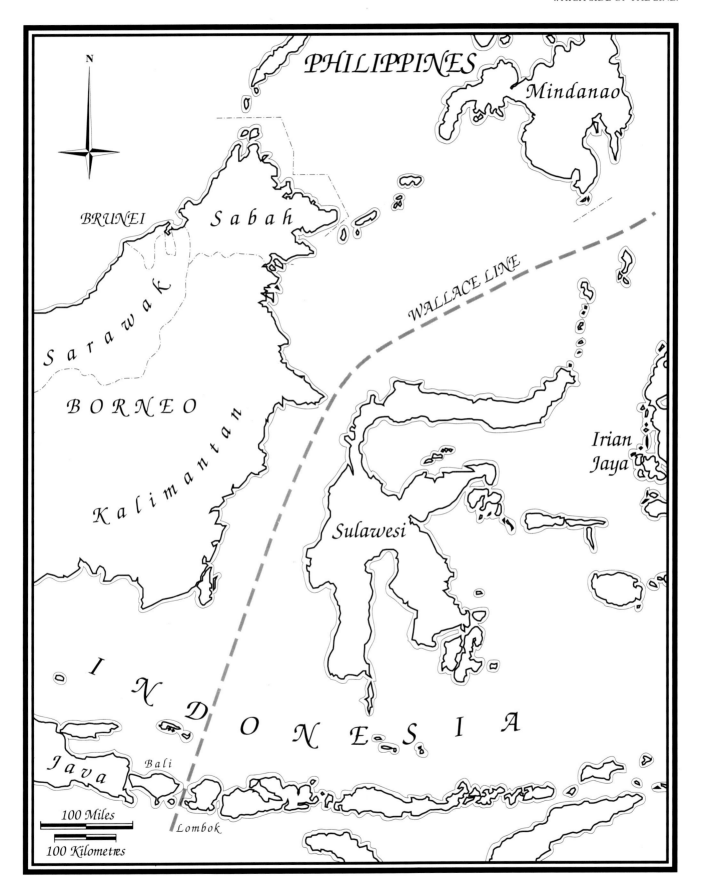

islands between these in the Australian Region. Between lay a no man's land with a truly puzzling flora and fauna. Most puzzling of all was the large star-shaped island then called Celebes and now part of Indonesia and known as Sulawesi. Though Wallace was inclined to draw his line round some of the islands with a blacker and firmer pencil than are modern zoologists, nevertheless the Wallace Line still stands where he put it, as the division between the two regions.

Wallace made his study over a century before the discovery of the now totally accepted theory of plate tectonics. This (see Introduction) explains the movement of whole continents as well as the occurrence of volcanic activity along the lines at which plates collide, subduct or separate. He drew a different conclusion from the vast amount of volcanic activity that takes place among the islands of South-East Asia. His ex-

Tapirs occur in South America as well as Asia. In Asia, they do not cross the Wallace Line into the Australian Region. The Malay tapir's foreparts and limbs are usually black and the body white. Tapirs frequent wet tropical forests.

Darwin and Wallace came to the same conclusion about archipelago birds. Even when islands are close together, species and sub-species seldom intermingle. Darwin's Galapagos Cactus Ground finch is one example.

(Previous page) Alfred Russel Wallace, a contemporary of Charles Darwin, defined the line that bears his name. It separates the oriental from the Australian Region. Animals and plants on each side of the line are quite different.

planation of the shallow shelves between the islands was that they were the result of subsidence caused by volcanic activity.

'It is also to be remarked,' wrote Wallace, 'that the great chain of active volcanoes in Sumatra and Java furnishes us with a sufficient cause for this subsidence, since the enormous masses of matter thrown out would take away the foundations of the surrounding district; and this may be the true explanation of the often-noticed fact that volcanoes and volcanic chains are always near the sea. The subsidence they produce around them will, in time, make a sea if one does not already exist.'

On the distribution of major species, however, he was completely accurate. He wrote: 'But it is when we examine the zoology of these countries that we find what we most require— evidence of a very striking character that these great islands must once have formed a part of the continent, and could only have been separated at a very recent geological epoch. The elephant and tapir of Sumatra and Borneo, the rhinoceros of Sumatra and the allied species of Java, the wild cattle of Borneo of the kind long supposed to be peculiar to Java, are now all known to inhabit some part or other of Southern Asia. None of these large animals could possibly have passed over the arms of the sea which now separates these countries, and their presence plainly indicates that a land communication must have existed since the origin of the species . . .'

Wallace observed that barbets occurred in Bali but were absent from Lombok island, 15 miles (24 km) away. This is a Brown-headed barbet (left).

The smallest of the five rhinoceros species, the Sumatran rhino (below). Its ancestors crossed from mainland Asia on a long-vanished land bridge.

'Turning our attention now to the remaining portion of the Archipelago, we shall find that all the islands from the Celebes and Lombok eastward exhibit almost as close a resemblance to Australia and New Guinea as the western islands do to Asia . . .'

And perhaps most interesting of all: 'The great contrast between the two divisions of the Archipelago is nowhere so abruptly exhibited as on passing from the island of Bali to that of Lombok, where the two regions are in closest proximity. In Bali we have barbets, fruit-thrushes and woodpeckers; on passing over to Lombok these are seen no more, but we have an abundance of cockatoos, honeysuckers and brush-turkeys which are equally unknown in Bali or any island further west. The strait is here fifteen miles [24 km] wide, so that we may pass in two hours from

The Great hornbill, largest of the world's many hornbill species, is a bird of the Oriental region. Typically, Sulawesi, the island that defies many of Wallace's rules of animal distribution, has two hornbill species of its own.

Brush turkeys, mound-building birds who hatch their eggs in compost heaps, belong to the Australian region. Wallace found them on Lombok, the island on the Australian side of his dividing line.

one great division of the earth to another, differing as essentially in their animal life as Europe does from America . . .'

Zoologists today might not agree that the division is quite so sharply defined as Wallace suggested. In fact, the elephants Wallace mentions never reached Borneo of their own accord. They were introduced there. Indeed he himself added a footnote to the paragraph quoted above: 'I was informed, however, that there were a few cockatoos at one spot on the west of Bali, showing that the intermingling of the productions of these islands is now going on . . .'

About the exchange of bird species between closely adjacent islands Wallace noted: 'Birds offer us one of the best means of determining the law of distribution; for though at first sight it would appear that the watery boundaries that kept out the land quadrupeds could be easily passed over by birds, yet practically it is not so; for if we leave out the aquatic tribes (seabirds) which are preeminently wanderers, it is found that the others (and especially the passeres, or perching birds, which form the vast majority) are often as strictly limited by straits and arms of the sea as are quadrupeds themselves.'

Wallace had come up with a great zoological truth. It applied equally to the Galapagos Archipelago where the ancestors of Darwin's finches had on arrival resolutely stuck to their islands and refused to travel short distances across water to interbreed and had consequently evolved into thirteen distinct species.

Monitor lizards defy most barriers to animal distribution, largely because they are excellent swimmers. The water monitor has a flattened tail for propulsion in water and nostrils at the tip of its nose to aid breathing when nearly submerged. The forked tongue is linked to olfactory organs. When it flicks out like this it is tasting or smelling the air. Monitors frequent both Oriental and Australian regions where they take many forms, including the giant Komodo Dragon on the Indonesian island of that name.

A water monitor swallows a fiddler crab (top). On Sulawesi, these lizards dig up the eggs of the increasingly rare maleo, a bird which buries its egg in the hot sand to hatch out.

(Bottom) Wallace noted that some cockatoos – Australian birds – had crossed his demarcation line to Bali. The division of species certainly isn't quite as definite as he supposed. However, the Great Black cockatoo, the largest Australian parrot, never ventures further west than New Guinea and northern Queensland.

The 'black ape' (right) is one of Sulawesi's many unique species. Although it is nearly tailless it is not an ape at all, but a monkey, otherwise known as the crested macaque.

(Previous page) The cuscus, a phalanger, and relative of the kangaroo, is found mainly in New Guinea but also among the mixed fauna of Sulawesi. The island has two species. They, more than anything else, pose the question: to which side of Wallace's line does Sulawesi belong?

Proof of the cuscus' close relationship to the kangaroo is the pouch for holding its young, common to all marsupials, also its comb-like hind claws which it shares with the kangaroo. Their possible purpose is for grooming (as above).

However when he came to Celebes (hereafter referred to by its modern name, Sulawesi), even Alfred Wallace was lost for a complete explanation of how this large star-shaped island acquired its fascinating and unusual fauna. Sulawesi breaks many of the rules of animal distribution in the archipelago. It lies centrally between Borneo and New Guinea yet owes complete faunal allegiance to neither. Modern zoologists put it in the Wallacean sub-region along with its adjacent islands, together with the Philippines (except Palawan and the Calamian group of islands) and the Lesser Sundas from Lombok to Timor. Sulawesi is situated midway between the shallow Sunda and Sahul shelves (see page 130). A simpler way of describing its position would be to say that it is part of the transitional zone between the Oriental and Australian regions. But, where wildlife is concerned, nothing in Sulawesi is ever simple!

Sulawesi and the rest of the Wallacean region have been isolated for at least several hundred thousand years. In this time some incredible things in terms of animal distribution and evolution have taken place there. The island has many species that indicate a strong link in the past with Asian wildlife but also a connection, although a weaker one, with Australian fauna. The latter includes birds and two species of marsupial, or pouched, mammals.

Wallace estimated that Sulawesi was of very ancient origin, possibly even dating from a time before Sumatra, Java and Borneo were raised above the level of the ocean. 'Such an antiquity,' he wrote, 'is necessary to account for the number of animal forms it possesses, which show no relation to those of India or Australia.'

Though the findings of modern geology relating to the origins of islands in the archipelago were not available to Wallace, his observations on the wildlife of Sulawesi can hardly be faulted.

He estimated that there were 108 species of land birds, only nine of which were found in islands to the westward and nineteen to the east. 'No less than 80 are entirely confined to the Celebesian fauna, a degree of individuality which, considering the situation of the island, is hardly to

be equalled in any other part of the world. . . .'

Of the eighty endemic species, eighteen are pigeons and of these eleven are found nowhere else in the world. Hornbills are distributed over much of Asia and Africa but the two Sulawesi species are unique to the island. Of the ten parrot species, eight are special to Sulawesi. The three woodpeckers are different from their nearest relatives in Java and Borneo. The list of endemic bird species is a lengthy one. The endemic mammals are fewer but even more striking in their differences from their nearest relatives in the Oriental or Australian regions.

There are fourteen terrestrial mammals and seven bat species. Of the land mammals, eleven are unique, including two that have almost certainly subsequently been introduced to nearby smaller islands by man. But there is no doubt that they evolved in Sulawesi.

The strangest of all must surely be the babirusa, a species of wild pig unlike any other pig

Undoubtedly the strangest of Sulawesi's amazing fauna, the babirusa, a species of pig with four tusks, two of which curve backwards over the head. No satisfactory explanation has been found for these.

Blue-throated barbet in its resting hole. The barbet species spread as far east as Bali but not into Lombok separated by only 15 miles (24 km) of water.

species on earth. The male babirusa has four tusks. The two in the lower jaw are long and sharp and slope backwards. The longer upper tusks grow upwards through the skin and curve backwards over the eyes. Local legend said that the animal used these to hang itself up from a low-hanging branch of a tree at night. Another theory was that the tusks protect the eyes when the babirusa is hunting for food among thorny undergrowth. This is not a satisfactory answer because the tuskless females find their food in exactly the same way as the males. It seems more likely that the tusks are used in hostile encounters between rival males, though, unlike the antlers of a deer, the babirusa's backward-curving armament does not appear to be best designed for fighting. In old males the tusks grow to a great length and are often broken, as if by combat, so there may be something in this theory.

The upland forests of the island are home to another unique species, generally known as the black ape. It looks very like a small gorilla and though it appears to be tailless, like an ape, it is in fact a monkey, closely related to the macaques. Its alternative name of crested macaque is a far more appropriate one. It has obvious Asian affiliations.

So does the anoa, found only on Sulawesi. The anoa is the smallest of all the wild cattle. It stands only 39 in (1 m) at the shoulder and is related to the water buffalo. It is a shy forest animal. Sadly, the forests of Sulawesi, as everywhere else in the Oriental Region, are under threat from the axe and now the logger's chainsaw.

Very few marsupials—pouched mammals—are found outside the Australian Region. Tree-living kangaroos got only as far as New Guinea. One marsupial, however, did make it to Sulawesi. The cuscuses are tree-dwelling marsupials of the possum family, with short limbs and prehensile tails. They are nocturnal and live on leaves, insects, small mammals and birds. The island has two species, the larger bear cuscus and the smaller Celebes cuscus. Their presence on the island once again poses the question: to which side of the Wallace Line does Sulawesi really belong?

(Left and overleaf) The seven species of tree kangaroo – this is Goodfellow's – are confined to New Guinea and northern Queensland. They are poor climbers but since there are no predators in the tree tops, they do not need to be particularly agile.

BIG-FOOTED BIRD

There can be no doubt from which side of the Wallace Line the ancestors of the maleos came. The maleo is a chicken-sized bird belonging to the megapode family. Megapode means 'big foot' and the 'big feet' are confined, with the exception of the maleos on Sulawesi, to the Australian Region.

The Australian megapodes are usually known as brush-turkeys or as mallee fowl after the mallee, the kind of semi-desert scrub that they frequent. The reason for the bird's big feet is that it needs a large shovel with which to pile up the mound of compost, earth and leaf litter in which the fowl buries and incubates its single very large egg. The egg is hatched without any direct help from either parent. Even more amazing than this remote-control brooding is the way in which it visits the mound at regular intervals and tests the temperature inside with its beak. It adjusts the heat needed to incubate the egg by adding to or subtracting from the amount of compost piled above it.

A mallee fowl on top of the mound in which it buries its egg. It tests the temperature daily and adjusts it by adding or subtracting compost.

The egg needs to be extremely large because it contains the nourishment required to produce a most precocious chick. When the young mallee fowl emerges, there are no parents around to feed or look after it. Having dug its way out of the compost heap, it must immediately start to fend for itself in the hostile world of the mallee scrub.

Alfred Wallace made a special expedition to study the mallee fowl's distant relation on Sulawesi, building a hut for his stay on a beach of coarse volcanic sand in the north of the island. His account can hardly be bettered:

'The appearance of the bird when walking on the beach is very handsome. The glossy black and rosy white of the plumage, the helmeted head and elevated tail, like that of the common fowl, give a striking character, which their stately and somewhat sedate walk renders still more remarkable. There is hardly any difference between the sexes, except that the casque or bonnet at the back of the head and tubercles at the nostrils are a little larger, and the beautiful rosy salmon colour a little deeper in the male bird . . .'

Studies are now being conducted into the habits of the maleo but so far ornithologists have added little since Wallace's day to our knowledge of the bird.

We now know that the casque to which Wallace referred is an extension of the bird's skull consisting of 'frothy' bone covered in skin. This appears to act as a sort of 'pith helmet' to protect the head from the tropical sun.

Each hen can lay up to thirty eggs but deposits each one in a different pit. Both parents help in the excavation of the pit, which can take up to three hours to dig. When one bird digs, the other stands on guard. This is probably where the 'sun hat' helps, since both birds evidently pant as they work.

Although several pairs often lay near each other, pits are vigorously defended against neighbours. Wallace's observation of up to thirty eggs in a nest therefore seems somewhat doubtful. In the northern parts of Sulawesi the maleos obviously know of the presence of hot underground streams, using the heat in the volcanic gravel to incubate their eggs. Elsewhere, as Wallace recorded, they dig their pits in the hot sand.

The maleos of Sulawesi have a number of natural predators. Wild pigs and monitor lizards dig up their eggs. Pythons prey on the newly emerged young. However, the most dangerous predator remains the same as in Wallace's day—man. There are only a few thousand maleos left, most of them in the northern parts of the island.

Fortunately, steps are being taken by the Indonesian wildlife department, assisted by the Worldwide Fund for Nature, to protect the remaining population and to increase it by artificial rearing. The pits where the birds have buried their eggs are quite easy to spot—as human predators have known for centuries—by the slight mounds left by the birds at the surface. Only the newest pits are excavated in order not to take eggs that have already started to develop.

The collected eggs are reburied at the headquarters of the maleo reserve at Panau and left to incubate naturally but protected from predators. In the wild the newly hatched chicks are most vulnerable when they emerge exhausted by their struggles to dig their way out of the sand.

Once hatched, the young maleos are easy to look after since they are fully active and able to feed themselves. After two days which give them time to gain maximum strength they are taken back and released in the same areas as the eggs were collected.

Alfred Russel Wallace was a contemporary of Charles Darwin whom he greatly admired. Though their work on evolutionary theory was complementary, Wallace has tended to become overshadowed by the religious and scientific furore that accompanied the publication of Darwin's The Origin of Species. *Wallace's own work* The Malay Archipelago *is nevertheless a classic in its own right.*

This mallee fowl chick (right) has just hatched and fought its way to the surface through its mound. Now it must fend for itself, without parental care.

This book has described how the marvellously rich and varied wildlife of the East inherited its kingdom, and how geology and climate have distributed the animals where they exist today. The last word must go to Alfred Russel Wallace, who so brilliantly understood the forces acting on this distribution and wrote over a century ago:

'The Celebes presents us with the most striking example of the interest that attaches to the study of the geographical distribution of animals. We can see that their present distribution upon the globe is the result of all the more recent changes the earth's surface has undergone; and by a careful study of the phenomena we are sometimes able to deduce approximately what those past changes must have been, in order to produce the distribution we find to exist.

'In the comparatively simple case of the Timor group of islands we were able to deduce these changes with some approach to certainty. In the much more complicated case of the Celebes we can only indicate their general nature, since we now see the result not of any single or recent change, but of a whole series of the later revolutions which have resulted in the present distribution of land in the Eastern Hemisphere.'

FURTHER READING

Billy Arjan Singh, *Tiger Haven*; Harper & Row, 1973

Jim Corbett, *The Man-Eaters of Rudraprayag*; OUP, 1989

Nicholas Courtney, *The Tiger, Symbol of Freedom*; Quartet, 1980

G M Henry, *A Guide to the Birds of Ceylon*; OUP, 1978

Boonsong Lekagul and Jeffrey A McNeely, *Mammals of Thailand*;
Boonsong Lekagul, Bangkok, 1988

John McKinnon, *Highlanders of Thailand*; OUP, 1986

Dieter Plage, *Wild Horizons*; Collins, 1980

James Emerson Tennant, *Ceylon*; 1859

Alfred Russel Wallace, *The Malay Archipelago*, 1869

The Living World of Animals; the Reader's Digest Association, 1978

PICTURE ACKNOWLEDGEMENTS

The publishers and author would like to thank the following sources for use of the photographs on the pages listed:

PAGE

6   Dieter and Mary Plage Survival Anglia
9   Dieter and Mary Plage Survival Anglia
10   Joe E Blossom Survival Anglia
13   Michael Pitts Survival Anglia
14   Joanna Van Gruisen Survival Anglia
17   Mike Price/Survival Anglia
18, 22, 23 Dieter and Mary Plage Survival Anglia
25   Dieter and Mary Plage Survival Anglia
27   Vivek R Sinha Survival Anglia
28   Ian Beames Ardea
29   Pat Morris Ardea
30, 32 Vivek R Sinha Survival Anglia
34, 35 Dieter and Mary Plage Survival Anglia
36   Vivek R Sinha Survival Anglia
37   Dieter and Mary Plage Survival Anglia
38, 39 Vivek R Sinha Survival Anglia
40   Richard Bailey Survival Anglia
41   Dieter and Mary Plage Survival Anglia
42   Vivek R Sinha Survival Anglia
44   Hulton Picture Company
45, 46, 49 Dieter and Mary Plage Survival Anglia
50   Deeble Stone Survival Anglia
51   Dieter and Mary Plage Survival Anglia
52   Deeble and Stone Survival Anglia
54   Kenneth W Fink Ardea
55   Bruce Davidson Survival Anglia
56   Dieter and Mary Plage Survival Anglia
57   Dieter and Mary Plage Survival Anglia
58   Vivek R Sinha Survival Anglia
59   Dieter and Mary Plage Survival Anglia (left)
     Joe Van Wormer Ardea (upper right)
     D & R Sullivan Bruce Coleman (lower right)
60   Dieter and Mary Plage Survival Anglia
62   Arjan Singh Survival Anglia
64   Dieter Plage Survival Anglia
65   Mike Price Survival Anglia
66, 67 Dieter and Mary Plage Survival Anglia
69   Vivek R Sinha Survival Anglia
70, 72, 74, 75 Dieter and Mary Plage Survival Anglia
71   Joanna Van Gruisen Survival Anglia
76   M Kavanagh Survival Anglia
77   Dieter and Mary Plage Survival Anglia
78   Dieter and Mary Plage Survival Anglia
79, 80, 81, 82, 85, 86, 88 Dieter and Mary Plage Survival Anglia
89   Mike Price Survival Anglia
91   Tan Ju Hock Survival Anglia
92   Joanna Van Gruisen Survival Anglia
94   Ashish Chandola Survival Anglia
95   Dieter and Mary Plage Survival Anglia
96   Vivek R Sinha Survival Anglia
97, 98 Dieter and Mary Plage Survival Anglia
100 Jeff Foott Survival Anglia
101 Vivek R Sinha Survival Anglia (top)
     Dieter and Mary Plage Survival Anglia (bottom)
102 Peter Clarke Survival Anglia
104 M Kavanagh Survival Anglia
107, 108, 110, 111 Dieter and Mary Plage Survival Anglia
113, 114 Michael Pitts Survival Anglia
115 Nick Gordon Survival Anglia
116, 117 Michael Pitts Survival Anglia
119 Pat Morris Ardea (top left)

PAGE

119 Jan and Des Bartlett Survival Anglia (top right)
     Michael Pitts Survival Anglia (bottom)
120 Dieter and Mary Plage Survival Anglia
121 Michael Pitts Survival Anglia
122 Dieter and Mary Plage Survival Anglia
123 Michael Pitts Survival Anglia
124 Jozef Mihok Survival Anglia
125 Michael Pitts Survival Anglia
127 Dieter and Mary Plage Survival Anglia
128 Dieter and Mary Plage Survival Anglia
129 Dieter and Mary Plage Survival Anglia
130 Peter Ward Bruce Coleman
131 Dieter and Mary Plage Survival Anglia
132 M Kavanagh Survival Anglia
133 Vivek R Sinha Survival Anglia
134 Mike Price Survival Anglia
135 Gerald Cubitt Bruce Coleman
136 Tan Ju Hock Survival Anglia
137 Dieter and Mary Plage Survival Anglia
138 Rod Williams Bruce Coleman
139 S C Bisserôt
140 Tan Ju Hock Survival Anglia
141 M Kavanagh Survival Anglia
142 P Morris Ardea
143 Mike Pitts Survival Anglia
144, 147 Dieter and Mary Plage Survival Anglia
148 Tony Beamish Ardea
149 Kenneth W Fink Ardea
150 Dieter and Mary Plage Survival Anglia
151 M Kavanagh Survival Anglia
152 Dieter and Mary Plage Survival Anglia
153 Dieter and Mary Plage Survival Anglia
154 Dieter and Mary Plage Survival Anglia
155 Dieter and Mary Plage Survival Anglia
156 M Kavanagh Survival Anglia (top)
     Dieter and Mary Plage Survival Anglia
158 Mike Price Survival Anglia
159 Dieter and Mary Plage Survival Anglia
160 M Kavanagh Survival Anglia
161 Dieter and Mary Plage Survival Anglia
162 M Kavanagh Survival Anglia
163 Mike Price Survival Anglia (top)
     Dieter and Mary Plage Survival Anglia
166 M Kavanagh Survival Anglia
167 Francois Guerout Ardea
168 Dieter and Mary Plage Survival Anglia
169 M Kavanagh Survival Anglia
170 P Morris Ardea
171 Des and Jen Bartlett Survival Anglia
172 Dieter and Mary Plage Survival Anglia
174 Dieter and Mary Plage Survival Anglia (top)
     Kenneth W Fink Ardea (bottom)
175 Alain Compost Bruce Coleman
176 Alan Root Survival Anglia
178 Eric Lindgren Ardea
179 Alain Compost Bruce Coleman
180 Joanna Van Gruisen Survival Anglia
181 Frithfoto Bruce Coleman
182 Frithfoto Bruce Coleman
183, 185 Des and Jen Bartlett Survival Anglia
184 Mary Evans/Society for Psychical Research

INDEX

Boxtree also publishes the following titles with Survival/Anglia:

THE SURVIVAL FACTOR
Mike and Tim Birkhead
This highly illustrated book discusses the fascinating characteristics that help animals to survive and reproduce in the face of natural selection, overcoming the adversities of their own environment.

ANTARCTICA
Dr Richard Laws
An introduction to the world's most isolated continent, which describes in stunning colour its unique natural history and its crucial scientific role in determining the ecological future of our planet.

KINGDOM OF THE DEEP
Colin Willock
A beautifully illustrated exploration of the ocean kingdom and some of the remarkable creatures that depend on its unique ecosystems.

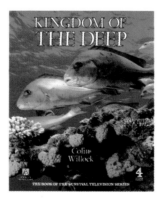